THE BATTLE OF THE BIRDS

and other Celtic tales

THE BATTLE

of the

BIRDS

and other Celtic tales

MARION LOCHHEAD

Illustrated by
PAT HANNAH

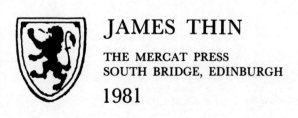

JAMES THIN

THE MERCAT PRESS
SOUTH BRIDGE, EDINBURGH

1981

© Marion Lochhead

James Thin
The Mercat Press
Edinburgh

ISBN 0 901824 63 1

Reproduced from copy supplied
printed and bound in Great Britain
by Billing and Sons Limited
Guildford, London, Oxford, Worcester

Contents

Preface

The Celtic Magic

In Celtic legend there are always the two countries: the actual Scotland, Ireland, Wales, or Brittany — and the land of enchantments lying close to it. To pass from one to the other is easy, dangerously easy. It may happen to a quite ordinary and humble character, or to a prince. They all live on the borders of magic, king and fisherman, prince, farmer, and miller.

Many of these stories are distinctly feminist. The hero plays his part very well — up to a point. Then he is set an impossible task, and the heroine has to come to his aid. She has courage, resourcefulness, and patience. Sometimes, within sight of a happy ending, the hero is bewitched and forgets; again the faithful girl must rescue him — as she does in *The Battle of the Birds* and in *The Brown Bear of Norway* — and forgive his lapse. It is rare for the heroine to slip; when she does, she makes full expiation. The princess in *The Brown Bear of Norway* is indeed misguided when she follows the advice of her mother and sisters (advice given, though they do not suspect this, by the witch) but she atones through her long journey, through patience and wisdom.

There is a casual air about some of the narratives; characters are brought in when wanted, then dismissed without further thought: the prince's three sisters in *The Brown Bear of Norway*, the raven's four sisters in *The Battle of the Birds*. In the *Brown Bear* they are protective and helpful, their gifts to the princess prove necessary to her rescue of her husband, but they pass out of the story. The raven's sisters give food and shelter to the prince who has saved their brother — then no more is heard of them or of him, nor are we offered any explanation of how he came to be bewitched into his bird form. And we are at a loss to understand how a cruel and ugly giant comes to have a kind and lovely daughter.

We are led into a magic country, and should accept people
and events as they come and not ask too many questions.

There is an extremely vague sense of time and place.
Seven years, twenty years — what does it matter so long as the
lost are found, the travellers come safely home in the end?

History and geography in these legends are anything but
precise studies. It would be difficult to trace a map of Macsen's
dream-journey, or to give the dates of his reign or that of
Lludd.

Perhaps the strongest element in Celtic legend is that of
The Good People or The Little People or the *Sidhe* (the word
fairy is not often used) who live in their green hill or rath,
sometimes in apparent splendour which may suddenly turn to
barrenness, the music silent, the lights quenched, the horses
turned into briars and branches. The boundary between their
realm and that of humans is very narrow, too close for the
good of humankind. Any day a child may be stolen away and a
changeling put in his place, and no kindness should be shown
to the changeling. There is a fair amount of ruthlessness. But
these creatures are neither human nor decent animals, they are
close to the demons.

As for animals and birds, there is understanding and
friendship between them and humans. The prince saves the
raven without knowing that he is a man under a spell. There is
mutual understanding in language, and this is never questioned.

Celtic mythology goes very far back in time. Gods and
heroes are near each other, as in classical mythology. The
heroes die, the gods are conquered by the new faith, though
they are never wholly banished, nor are the heroes forgotten.

There is another border besides that between the magic
and the actual worlds. As the stories were carried into
Christian times the new light touched them. This is especially
notable in some of the Irish stories. That excellent fellow
Guleesh, having helped to rescue the Princess of France from
her heartless parents and her detested bridegroom, finds he
must save her from a worse evil — from the power of the Little
People. He signs her with the cross in the Name of God. Then
he takes her to the priest, who receives and protects her until
the last vestige of magic is overcome; and then — a happy

marriage. The fisherman also takes his bride to the priest to make them man and wife, even though she is not wholly human. MacEachern, that best of fathers, goes bravely into the rath to deliver his son, protected by the Bible he carries.

When the great missionary saints, Patrick and Columba, brought the Gospel to Ireland and to Scotland they encountered the old magic. The most dramatic encounter is that between Patrick and Oisin, son of the great Fionn, last of the Finians. Long, long before, he had met and loved the fairy woman Niamh and gone with her into Tir-n'an-Og, the Land of the Ever-Young, where time is not counted. But on earth it *does* count, and when Oisin returned he was himself of incredible age, and all his comrades had long since died, only a shadowy remembrance left. He met Patrick, who took him to his own house and tried to convert him to the new faith. But Oisin was reluctant. He uttered a great lament for Fionn and his heroes; he asked Patrick many questions. Were he admitted to the paradise of the king whom Patrick worshipped, would he be allowed to take with him his dogs and his hounds, dear and faithful companions? Patrick answered sternly that the King of Glory would not permit them to enter. So that would be no heaven for Oisin; he would not abandon his faithful followers. Many centuries later a great Christian poet and storyteller would have assured him of a heavenly welcome for his dogs: George MacDonald believed that they, and horses, and all God's creatures returned to their maker and were blessed.

Saint Columba, although stern, was generous. He encountered the power of the druids, guardians of the old magic. When he came to the fortress of King Brude, on Loch Ness, he found the doors were barred against him, it may be with an added strength of druidic force. But he made the sign of the cross on the doors, and laid his hand on them commanding them to open, and they flew wide apart for his entrance.

He reproved the druid Broichan for keeping captive an Irish girl. When Broichan refused to set her free Columba prophesied that illness and death would fall upon him. The saint departed, and Broichan fell mortally ill with a stroke. Messengers came hurriedly begging for a miracle of healing, promising in Broichan's name that the girl would be set free. Columba had taken a white stone from the river; he blessed it, gave it to the messengers, bidding them drop it into a cup of water and give it to the druid to drink. Two of Columba's companions went back with the messengers. The stone did not sink, but floated in the water. The druid drank — and was cured. The girl set free was brought to the saint to be looked after.

The third of the great Celtic saints is Brigit, Bride of Kildare; historically she belongs to the 5th and 6th centuries. She was learned and wise, she founded the Abbey of nuns of Kildare. The story tells that she was also a shepherdess, Bride of the Isles, in Scotland, and that she lived at the very dawn of the new faith.

On that night of nights which brought the world's salvation she was carried by angels to Bethlehem to help Our Lady in childbed, and to hold the Lamb of God in her arms.

Saint Bride the herd-maiden
Was taken, they say,
To nurse the Lord Jesus
Asleep in the hay.

She was carried again to her own islands, to care again for the lambs and for the babies whom she received and cherished,

And sang, as she nursed them:
"Who holds you, but she
Who held the Lord Jesus
Asleep on her knee."

SCOTLAND

Scotland shares with Ireland two of the great and sorrowful love
stories of the world: that of Deirdre and Naoise, and that of
Grania and Diarmid. They share, too, the danger of the fairy hill
or rath, and of changelings. Birds and beasts perhaps appear more
often in the Scottish tales; and the minor character who helps, like
the good shoemaker in The Battle of the Birds, is rather a Scottish
type — he may even, with his silly wife and daughter, have been
drawn from life.

The Battle of the Birds

It all began with a quarrel between a wren and a mouse. The wren had met a farmer out walking and looking worried.

"What ails you?", asked the wren.

"I'm trying to find a servant to begin the threshing, and I've had no luck."

"Take me", said the wren.

"You! A wee bit of a creature like you?", the farmer laughed.

"Try me", urged the wren, and the farmer did; he took the wren to his barn, the wren began threshing. He threshed one grain of barley and a mouse came out of its hole and ate it.

"Don't do that again", the wren told him, and threshed two grains of barley. The mouse ate those.

"I told you not to do that again", said the wren angrily. "If your do, there will be trouble."

He threshed three grains of barley and the mouse ate them too.

So there was nothing for it but a battle between birds and beasts, both of all sizes, from near and far.

3

It was a great battle and a long one, and news of it spread all over the country. In one part, a long way away, the king of that place was out walking with his son.

"It must be a queer battle", he said. "I'd like to hear more of it".

"And so you should", agreed his son. "Aren't you the king of all these creatures? I'll go and see what I can of it, and bring you the news."

He set off very early and walked all day, at first guided by the noise and by the sight of the birds flying overhead; but when he came to the place of the battle late in the evening, it was all over; not a creature was to be seen but a raven and a snake. The snake was coiled round the raven's neck, the raven had the snake's throat in his beak. The prince did not like snakes, so he drew his sword, cut off its head, and released the raven from its coils.

"You're a friend and hero", the bird told him. "You've saved my life, and I'm not one to forget that. Now, do you see that house over there with the light in the window? Go you there; the woman of the house is my sister. She will ask if you have seen me today. Tell her you have and that I am well. She will give you a good welcome, water for your feet, food and fire, and a bed for the night. And tomorrow meet me at sunrise, and I'll take you on a flight over nine glens and nine bens."

The prince thanked him and walked to the house. He was kindly received, the woman of the house asked whether he had seen her brother and he told her yes, and that all was well. Then she made a fine supper for him by the fire, bathed his tired feet, and sent him to bed for a good night's sleep. In the morning at sunrise he was at the meeting-place. The raven swooped down, took him up on his back, and flew over nine glens and nine bens.

"That was fine; thank you kindly", said the prince when the raven set him down.

"Tomorrow I will take you over six glens and six bens", promised the raven. "But now, go over to that house there, with the light in the window. The woman is my second sister. She will ask if you have seen me, and you must tell her yes, and that all is well. You will have a great welcome from her too.

And meet me here tomorrow at sunrise."

The prince obeyed. The woman of the house welcomed him, asked whether he had seen her brother, and he told her yes, and that all was well. Again he had a good supper by the fire, water for his feet, a warm bed and a full night's sleep. At sunrise he was at the meeting-place; the raven swooped down, took him on his back and flew with him over six glens and bens. Again he set him down, again the prince thanked him kindly, again the raven bade him go to a house nearby. There again a kind woman received him, asked whether he had seen her brother, and again the prince told her yes, and that all was well. For the third night he had a good welcome, food and fire, water for washing, a warm bed and sound sleep. In the morning for the third time he met the raven, as he had been bidden. Their flight this day was short; over three glens and bens. When the raven set him down he bade him go to a house within sight, where he would be well recieved. Again this was true, again he was asked by the kind woman whether he had seen her brother, and he told her yes, and that all was well. The raven had bidden him meet him again at sunrise, and again, after a good night, he was there; but no raven came flying over or swooping down.

A young man came walking along, a fine handsome fellow, well-dressed, and carrying a large bundle. The prince asked him very politely if he had seen a raven flying anywhere near.

"It's myself that was the raven", said the young man. "And now I am freed from the enchantment that held me, and am myself again. It is you have set me free; and here is your reward."

He gave the prince the bundle he was carrying.

"Go your way home now, and when you come to the place you like best of all, open the bundle — but not before. Now farewell, and my thanks and my blessing be with you."

"And mine with you", the prince replied courteously, and walked off. He walked all day, happily enough, but at dusk he began to feel weary. He was, he knew, not very far from his father's palace, but his way lay through a dark wood; his bundle was very heavy, he set it down for a moment.

"I might as well have a look", he thought. "I'll not open it wide."

He opened it just a chink, but then it opened itself wide; and out of the bundle appeared a palace set in a garden with an orchard beyond. Palace, garden, and orchard grew at once to a great size. It would be impossible ever to get them back into the bundle, and this was not at all the place where the poor foolish prince wanted to be.

He blamed himself for his folly. He was near weeping, when he heard the thud of feet so heavy as to shake the ground, and saw a great giant coming towards him.

"What ails you?", roared the giant.

"My own folly", said the prince. "I've opened the bundle here, where no one would wish to bide, and I'll never get this palace and all back into it. And the place I would really wish to be is the wide green valley near my father's palace."

"What will you give me if I bundle all this up and let you have it again?", asked the giant.

"What would you have?".

"Your first-born son when he is seven years old", said the giant.

Without thinking, the prince, who was not married or even betrothed and had no possible bride in his mind, replied:

"If ever I have a son, you may have him when he comes to seven years."

The giant touched palace and garden and orchard, and at once they dwindled to the small size they had been; he tied them all up in the bundle and handed it to the prince.

"Away with you now, and I'll be going my own way. Don't be forgetting your promise. If you do forget, I'll come and remind you."

He went away, and the prince continued his journey until he came to that fair green valley where he longed to be, and where he really wanted to stay. Here again he opened his bundle. The palace and garden and orchard appeared, they grew to a fine and stately size, and the prince forgot all his tiredness, and hardly remembered his stupid impatience and what he had promised the giant.

He was within sight of his father's palace, and went there to a joyful welcome from the king and queen, his father and mother. He told them all his adventures, they feasted together, and the prince slept well that night in his own room. Next morning he walked over to the green valley where his own fine palace stood in its garden and orchard. As he came to the door it was opened to him by the most beautiful girl he had ever seen, and she was smiling a welcome. He fell in love at the very sight of her, and she with him. The king and queen were well pleased when he brought her to see them, so they were married that very day and went to live in their own palace.

A year passed, and a fine son was born to them. Three or four more years passed and the old king and queen died, after a long and happy life together. So the prince and his bride were king and queen themselves now, living sometimes in the old palace but most of the time in their own; the little prince grew into a fine lad, and before they knew where they were it was his seventh birthday. They made a great feast for him and were joyful together, for the young king had forgotten all about the promise he had made to the giant. But next morning there was a great thud of feet outside, and the giant came up to the palace, opened the door and demanded:

"Let me have your son as you promised."

Certainly you must have him", said the king. "Just let me go and tell the queen, and she will bring him to you."

He told the queen, who was careful not to reproach him, for she knew that would not help at all. She was a clever woman and quickly thought of a plan. Sending for the cook's son, who was of the same age as the prince, she dressed him in fine clothes, led him to the giant whom she greeted politely, kissed the boy and handed him over. They walked off together; but the giant was no fool, and presently he said to the boy:

"If your father had a stick like this one I'm carrying, what would he do with it?".

The boy replied innocently:

"He'd beat the dogs and cats that come into the kitchen, and drive them away from the king's dinner."

The giant roared with fury, beat the poor boy with the stick, threw him into the ditch, and strode angrily away. After a time the boy crept out and ran home, crying.

Next morning there was the thudding of feet and a bang

at the door, and the giant's voice shouting:

"I've come for your son, and you'd better let me have him this time".

"You shall have him," the king replied. "His mother is dressing him, and will bring him to you".

The queen was indeed dressing a boy in one of the fine suits of the prince, but it was not the prince himself she was dressing. This time it was the son of the butler. The giant walked off with him; and before they had gone very far he asked:

"If your father had this stick I have in my hand, what would he do with it?".

Innocently the poor little boy told him:

"He would beat the cats and dogs that tried to come into the king's wine-cellar."

"So you're the butler's son as the other boy was the cook's", roared the giant. "You'll soon wish you weren't here."

And again he beat the poor child mercilessly, and threw him into the ditch. After a while, the boy crept out and ran home sobbing.

Next morning there was a great angry roar outside the door of the palace.

"I've come for your son, and this time I'll have him and no one else. If you try to cheat me again you will suffer, you and all your house."

The king and queen knew they were defeated. The prince himself was handed over to the giant. As they walked, the giant asked:

"If your father had the stick I have in my hand, what would he do with it?"

"He would hold it as his sceptre when he sits on the throne", was the reply, and the giant knew that at last this was the true prince.

He took him to his own castle, a huge grim place it was, and kept him there. The giant was not unkind on the whole, and the little prince grew up into a fine strong man; but he never forgot his own home, his mother and father and their kingdom. Some day he would return there, though he would have to wait for the opportunity. For the present, however, there seemed little chance of escaping, for he was kept closely guarded.

One day, however, the giant went off on his own affairs, which were probably evil. The prince thought it a good opportunity to explore the huge castle. He climbed the great stairs, another stair beyond, and there he heard music — harp music, lovely and sweet such as had never heard since he was a little boy in his father's palace. He loved music, and the sounds seemed to draw him irresistably — up another stair, a steep and narrow one that brought him to an attic; the music was clear and loud and very near; he walked into the attic and saw there a beautiful girl, playing the harp. She smiled at him.

"You are welcome, prince. I know all about you. I am Mairi, the giant's youngest daughter, and I know how you long to escape. Now I can help you, and you can help me too, for my father is going to marry me to a man whom I cannot bear. Will you take me with you?"

"I shall indeed, for I love you, and you will be my bride."

"Listen, then, and do exactly as I tell you. Tonight, when my father returns, tell him that you want to return home. He will agree, on condition that you marry one of my two elder sisters. You must tell him you will have neither; you will marry only his youngest daughter. Now I shall play for you on my harp, and then you must go away, for you must not be found here."

She played again, entrancingly, and the prince listened in delight. They kissed each other and vowed to be faithful one to the other, for ever.

The giant came home, the prince went to him and begged leave to go back to his own kingdom.

"We'll see about that", growled the giant.

Next morning he summoned the prince; "You may return home", he said, "and you may take a bride with you: one of my two daughters, whichever you like. And here they come."

The prince hardly looked at the two daughters, but answered bravely:

"I choose neither. I will marry your youngest daughter."

The giant roared with rage; then he was quiet for a moment.

"Very well, then, so be it; but only after you have performed three tasks which I shall set you."

"What are they?" asked the prince.

"Come and see" — and the giant led him out to a byre in the yard.

"Every night a hundred cattle are sheltered here, and the place has not been cleaned for seven years. If you can clean it by morning, you will be one task nearer winning your bride and your freedom. If not, I shall kill you."

The giant laughed, and his laughter was not pleasant to hear. "I shall be away all day. If, when I come home, the byre is so clean that a golden apple might be rolled from one end to the other and not show a smear of dirt — then you may have a night's rest, and tomorrow will bring another task."

He went away, and the prince set bravely to work; but the floor and walls of the byre were so thick with filth that, though he toiled for hours on end with buckets of water and brushes and shovels, he seemed to be no nearer achieving his goal, and he was completely exhausted. Then the giant's youngest daughter came in:

"My poor love! You have been very valiant. Now come with me and sit under a tree and rest."

"I may as well be happy for an hour or two", thought the prince. "I am to be killed in any case."

The girl led him to a green bank under a tree. There he lay down and soon fell asleep. When he awoke, she had gone; he walked to the byre — and found it so clean that a golden apple might be rolled from one end to the other and never be soiled or stained. As the prince looked at it, amazed, he heard the giant come stamping and roaring along.

The giant stood in the doorway and glowered with fury.

"Who cleaned it?", he demanded. "Well, it was not you who cleaned it anyway!" said the prince. The giant said no more, and the prince went to his own room. He saw no one that night.

Early next morning the giant roared to him to come out. He led him back to the byre.

"Today you will thatch this place with feathers from so many birds that no two feathers will be of the same colour. If you succeed, you will have one task more before you may marry my daughter. If you fail — well, there will be no need for any further task."

The giant laughed his horrible laugh and went away on some evil business or other. The prince fetched his bow and arrows and walked off to a moor where many birds flew. But luck was against him; he shot down only two blackbirds and their feathers were of the same colour.

Then the giant's youngest daughter came to him.

"My poor love, you are weary. Come over to this green bank and lie down and sleep."

"I am likely to have a long bitter sleep tonight", said the prince sadly. "I may as well sleep pleasantly now."

He lay down where she led him and fell asleep. When he awoke there was no sign of the girl; but when he walked to the byre he saw the roof thatched with a multitude of feathers, and no two feathers were of the same colour.

As he gazed at this marvel, the giant came thumping and stamping along,

"Who did this?", he roared. "I am sure you could not have done it!" replied the prince.

"We'll see what you can do tomorrow", growled the giant. "Your task then will be bring to me the eggs from the magpie's nest in that tree over there", and he pointed to a very tall tree thick with branches near the top, but with none anywhere near the foot. The giant laughed:

"I want those eggs for my supper. If you bring them, I might give you one. If not — well you won't be needing any supper."

He went off roaring with laughter, and the prince went quietly to bed, to sleep as well as he could. When he came to the tree early next morning he found as he had feared: the tall smooth trunk rose high above him with neither foot-hold nor hand-hold.

"You will never climb that without help", said the youngest daughter, coming up behind him. "But I can help. Just watch what I do and try not to shudder, then do exactly what I tell you."

She began pulling off her fingers, one by one, and throwing them up into the tree trunk, where they stuck and stuck out, lengthening themselves into spars. The first was only a good stride from the ground, the tenth was up at the top branches.

"Climb now, my love", said the girl. "Take the eggs carefully and come down; and do not forget to draw out each finger in turn as you descend."

Quickly the prince climbed, carefully he gathered the eggs from the nest, wrapping them in his handkerchief, and putting them into his pocket. Then he began to climb down, carefully, without slipping; as he came he drew out every finger, one by one, all except one: the little finger at the top. He was in such haste that he forgot this one.

"Well done", said the girl smiling at him. She took the fingers from him and put them back on her hands where they became small and slender again.

"But one is missing; the little one of this hand".

"I forgot to bring it. Please forgive me!"

"No matter; the other four will serve me well enough. And indeed it may be as well I have only four. Tonight my father will put you to a test. He will have my sisters and me brought into the room, all dressed alike, with veils over our faces, and will bid you take your bride. You will see my hand with the little finger missing, and you will know."

It happened just as she said. The giant came home, sat down to supper, and saw the eggs on a dish before him.

"So you have finished your tasks", he roared. "Well now, you must choose your bride."

The three girls came into the room, all dressed exactly alike, all veiled. But at once the prince saw the hand which lacked a finger.

"This is my bride", he said, and he was allowed to lead her away.

"A room is prepared for us", she whispered, "but we shall not sleep there or anywhere tonight, for we are still in great danger. Come with me."

She led him to the stable where a strong grey filly was waiting, saddled and bridled. They mounted and rode away swiftly; but they had not gone far when the girl said:

"My father is riding after us. I can feel his breath hot on the back of my neck. Put your finger into the left ear of the filly and bring out what you find."

The prince obeyed and brought out a twig of blackthorn.

"Throw it behind us." He did this and the twig grew into a thick wood. The giant stopped, but not for long. He had a great axe at his belt and he soon cut down all the trees.

"My father is after us again; his breath is burning the back of my neck. Put your finger into the filly's right ear and bring out what you find."

The prince brought out a stone.

"Throw it behind us." The stone fell and became a great wall of rock. The giant halted, but not for long. He had a huge mattock with him and with this he smashed the rock wall.

"My father is still coming after us; his breath has nearly burned a hole in the back of my neck. Put your finger again into the filly's left ear, and bring out what you find."

The prince found a bladder of water.

"Throw it behind us." The bladder burst, the water spread and spread and spread into a great loch. The giant fell head-long into it, and was drowned.

And now the prince and his bride were within his father's kingdom, even within sight of the palace. The horse stopped at a well under a great tree.

"Ride on now my love to the palace, and tell the king and queen your father and mother all your adventures; tell them about me. I shall wait for you here, by the well. They will be overjoyed to see you; but one thing I beg do not let them or anyone else kiss you. A kiss would bring forgetfulness."

The prince promised. He rode on, came to the palace, and found his parents indeed joyful almost beyond words to see him. They would have embraced and kissed him but he held them off, telling them that a kiss was, for the time, forbidden. They accepted this. But just then the prince's old dog, who had been little more than a puppy when he was take away, came running out. He knew his master at once, and leapt up to lick him on the face. At once the prince's mind became blank of all memory of his adventures.

Beside the well his princess waited, and waited, and waited. She realised what must have happened. Night had fallen, and she climbed up into the branches of the tree above the well.

Next morning a woman came to draw a jugful of the clear

water. She was the wife of a shoemaker who lived near. As she bent over the well she saw, reflected as in a mirror, a most lovely face. Now she had never seen herself, having no looking glass at home.

"Can that be myself?" she exclaimed. "It must be, the water shows me so clearly. Never did I think I was so beautiful."

Forgetting to draw any water she ran home, leaving the jug behind.

"Where's the water?", asked her husband. "I'd like a drink."

"Then you can go and fetch it", said his wife haughtily. "Do you think a beautiful woman like me is going to fetch water for the likes of you? I've just seen myself in the well. Why did you never tell me I was so beautiful?"

The shoemaker might have retorted: "Because you are nothing of the sort", but he was a wise man and said no more, except to ask his daughter to fetch some water. The girl ran off, picked up the jug, and bent down over the well to dip it in. Then she saw that lovely face and thought:

"Why did my parents never tell me I was so beautiful? Why did no one tell me?" She ran home. "Where's the jug of water?" asked her father. "You can go and find it", she retorted rudely. "Don't you know you have a beautiful daughter, as beautiful as the queen herself?" The shoemaker knew nothing of the sort, but he was a wise man, and said nothing. The two women decided to give up housework and go off into the town to buy some finery. The cobbler went off by himself to the well, picked up the jug, bent over the water, and saw the lovely face. Of course he knew at once that he was not looking at his own reflection, so he looked up into the branches of the tree and saw the girl there.

"Will you not come down?" he asked her gently. "It is not very comfortable for you up there. Let me take you back to my house and give you a meal; and then you can rest for a time".

The girl came down, thanked the good man warmly, and came with him — and he did not forget the jug of water. He asked no questions, but set food and drink on the table for her, and she offered to do any work for him that was needed.

When his wife and daughter came back from the town they did not make her very welcome, but neither did they throw her out, in fact they hardly noticed her, for they were so taken up with their own finery. If she chose to stay — well she could do all the chores about the house, which were now beneath their notice. So she stayed and was a great help. The shoemaker was a very busy man, for he was an excellent craftsman and had always made shoes for many of the people about the court. Now he was told that the young prince had come home, and was soon to be married to a bride, chosen for him by the king and queen. It was said that he did not appear to take much interest in the affair himself. His adventures had perhaps exhausted him, for he was said to be very quiet and withdrawn.

The poor deserted girl heard all this.

"How I should like to see the prince and his bride", she said.

"And so you will. Tomorrow I have to take all these shoes up to the palace. You must come with me. There are to be great celebrations and there will be wine for everyone, to drink the health of the prince and his bride."

So next morning they walked up to the palace, carrying the shoes. They were kindly welcomed by some of the servants, and brought into the great hall, where all who came were given wine to drink the health of the prince and his bride. The king and queen were there, the bride and her father and mother; and the prince, who sat very quiet and withdrawn.

The shoemaker drank his wine, the girl put her lips to her glass but did not drink. She just whispered something, and out of the glass flew two pigeons — one silver, and one golden. From somewhere, three grains of wheat fell to the ground in front of the prince; the silver pigeon swooped down on them.

"Please, will you let me have one grain", begged the golden pigeon. "Do you not remember that I cleaned out the byre for you?"

The prince looked bewildered — but he looked at the girl.

Other three grains fell, and again the silver pigeon swooped down on them. "Will you not let me have one grain?" pleaded the golden pigeon. "Do you not remember how I thatched the byre with feathers, for you?" Again the prince looked at her, puzzled, yet as if he were trying to recall something.

Again three grains fell on the floor, and yet again the silver pigeon swooped down, and the golden one pleaded:

"Please give me one grain. Do you not remember how I gave you my fingers to climb the tree — and you left one behind, and see this hand is without its little finger!"

The pigeons vanished, the girl stood there holding out her hand, the prince looked and remembered everything. He came to her and took her in his arms.

"This is my true love and bride", he declared. "And now I can recall all my adventures."

They were married that day, the prince and his lovely brave girl.

What the other girl and her parents thought and said has not been recorded. Things happened like that often enough in those days, so they probably went home, and the girl probably found another bridegroom.

The king and queen welcomed their daughter-in-law with love and joy, and this was the beginning of years and years of happiness.

The odd thing is that no one remembers what happened to the wren and the mouse, whose quarrel began the whole carfuffle!

Deirdre

Colum the harper was of great fame in Erin for the beauty of his harping. He played every kind of tune, the joyful and the sorrowful, and some he played while chanting an old poem or legend. So he was welcomed everywhere he went, and was paid with gold or with silver or with jewels or fine garments; whatever he was given he received courteously, whether a rich gift or a small. His wife and he lived happily together as they had for many years, for they were long past their youth. They had only one grief: they had no children, and had longed for them for many a year. Colum would have delighted in a son to whom he could teach harping, his wife sadly wished for a daughter to whom she would have taught fine embroidery and all the household skills. But there was no hope of that now.

One day a soothsayer came to their house on his journeying. They gave him a kind welcome, and he told them something about the ways he had travelled and the people he had met.

"Can you foresee what is to come?", asked Colum. "Can you tell us what may happen to ourselves?"

The soothsayer was silent for a moment; then he said: "Let me go out by myself to meditate."

He went out, and after a while came in again.

"Have you a child?", he asked. "Have you a daughter?'

"We have no child at all, nor ever had one. And this has always been a great grief to us."

"That is strange; for I have seen in my sight of the future that your daughter will be the most beautiful of women, but that she will bring great sorrow and shedding of blood through her beauty."

"But that cannot be", declared Colum. "My wife is now long past child-bearing."

"That may be; but that is what I have seen, and I have never yet seen anything that has not come to pass."

He went away then, leaving Colum and his wife troubled, half-incredulous, half-believing.

The soothsayer had indeed spoken truth, for Colum's wife soon found herself with child.

He made a plan to turn aside the evil that had been

prophesied. In a remote place by a wood there was a large green mound. Here he brought workmen whom he put under a vow of secrecy, and had them hollow the mound, line it well, fit it with wood, and make it dry and warm. He had beds brought there and a table and stools, as well as all other necessary cooking and household utensils.

His wife's time came near, and he brought a wise woman to help her, called Lavarcham. In due time a daughter was born, and Colum named her Deirdre which means sorrow. He bade Lavarcham come with him, carrying the baby, to the sheiling he had made from the green mound.

"Here you must stay, seeing no one. I myself shall bring you stores of food and of clothes. But no one must know of this place or of this child."

He kept his promise, and Deirdre was kept there and cherished by Lavarcham, who knew a great many things: about birds and beasts, plants and flowers and trees, all the life of the woods. She taught Deirdre all her skills. And the child grew to girlhood, and if she had been lovely as a child, in her earliest infancy, she grew even lovelier every year. There had been none to match her in all the ages of Erin, among all the fair women.

She was happy too, for she loved the life of the woods; no one ever came near, and she was free as the air. But one night one of the huntsmen of the king, Conachur of Ulster, came that way; he had spent a long day in hunting, and he was weary and cold almost to death. Here at least, he thought, was the shelter of a mound; he lay down close to it and fell asleep, but not deeply or for long. He awoke thinking he heard sounds from within the mound: the stir of movement, the murmur of voices, very faint. Was he dreaming? He struggled to his feet, walked round, and came to a low wooden door: knocking loudly he called out:

"Let me in, let me in! I am perishing with cold. In the name of the Good Being, let me in!"

"What is that sound?" asked Deirdre.

"It is only one bird calling to another", said Lavarcham.

There was another knock on the door, and a cry.

"Let me in. I am dying. Let me in!"

"What is that?" asked Deirdre again.

"It is the cry of birds flying away into the wood", answered Lavarcham.

"But it was a cry for help — and in the name of the Good Being", said Deirdre. "And you have taught me always to answer a cry from bird or beast. I shall let it in, whatever it may be."

Deirdre opened the door and the man stumbled in. She put a seat for him by the fire, and brought food and drink.

"Rest now, for a little, for indeed you have been near perishing", she told him gently.

"I was indeed; but now your beauty has put away from me all my weariness, even my desire for food and drink."

"Will you be quiet", Lavarcham said sternly. "You came here for food and shelter and these you shall have. But at daybreak you must go, and you must forget what you have seen and heard, and vow never to speak of it."

"I promise", the man replied humbly. "But och, I could tell you of some who would have their hearts full of joy at seeing your beauty."

"And who are they?" asked Deirdre, not looking at Lavarcham, who was frowning at her and shaking her head.

"They are the three sons of Usnach; Naoise, Aillean, and Ardan, and they are the finest youths and the bravest that ever walked the woods and ways of Erin or Alba or sailed the sea between. They are tall and broad of shoulder, supple and swift of limb. Their hair is black as the raven's wing, their cheeks clear red. They can swim like the salmon, they can stride the hills like the young deer, and of the three, the tallest and the comeliest is Naoise."

"It is nonsense that you are talking. Sleep now, and when I wake you, depart", Lavarcham told him very sternly.

The man lay down before the hearth and fell asleep. Lavarcham kept awake. Very early in the morning she roused him, opened the door and bade him go.

"Small joy have you brought us; good it is that you go and do not return. My curse on you if you speak a single word of what you have seen here."

The man departed. He came to the palace of Conachur the king, his master. He had meant to keep silence, but he could not resist telling his comrades of his adventure: of the hidden green mound, and of the girl who lived there and her great beauty.

The tale came to the king who had no queen, and he ordered the huntsman to be brought to him.

"What is this adventure you have had? Whom did you see?"

"I saw a woman lovelier than any, more lovely than even the most beautiful lady here in your court. I shall never see anyone so lovely again."

"Where does she dwell?"

"In a green shieling within a wood."

"Can you take me there?"

"I can, my lord."

Next morning the cold weather with wind and rain that had come that night upon the huntsman in the woods was over, and it was a beautiful May morning. The king rose early and summoned his close band of kinsmen and attendants. He told them of the journey on which the huntsman would lead them, and they all set out walking in the freshness and fragrance of that dawn; the birds sang in the trees and bushes, the leaves and flowers glistened with dew, the branches stirred faintly. They walked through this gentle world to the glen and the wood where Deirdre and Lavarcham dwelt in solitude in their green shieling.

"There it stands, down there", the huntsman told them. "And now I shall be taking myself off, for I have no wish to meet that nurse woman again."

Off he went — he had done his task — and Conachur and his men came to the green mound and called out.

"Whoever you may be go away and do not disturb us", Lavarcham answered. "I am opening the door to no one."

"Do you know who is here?" called one of the men.

"I care not. I shall open to no one save Conachur the king himself, and I do not think it is he who calls."

"But I *do* call, and bid you open to me. I am Conachur himself", the king told her.

The poor woman was afraid to disobey, so she opened the door and the king entered. He looked at Deirdre and stood amazed, as if spellbound. Never had he seen or dreamed of such loveliness. There was only one thought in his mind; he *must* have her as his queen.

"You will come with me", he said to her, "to a house finer than you have ever seen. And you too shall come to be with her", he told Lavarcham, who was in two minds, not knowing whether to be afraid or to be glad. For life in the green shieling had little splendour to offer.

At a word from the king two of his men lifted Deirdre on to their shoulders, while two others carried Lavarcham. They returned to the palace; and there Deirdre and Lavarcham were lodged in a fine house. Conachur asked Deirdre to be his queen. She did not desire this, for she was afraid; but afraid also to refuse.

"Let me have time, my lord king. I know nothing of the world, nothing of all the arts a queen should have."

"That is well thought", Conachur agreed. He appointed ladies to wait upon her, to teach her all that a queen should know: how to sing and play sweet music on the harp; needlework; the ways of a palace; how to deal with servants. Lavarcham was to be with her, and she too was given a woman to attend her.

Fine and rich clothes were brought, the new life was one of great comfort and splendour. The weeks passed, and the months. The king was patient and waited his time.

One day of sunshine and blossoming flowers and tender green leaves Deirdre was playing with some of her attendants on a green hill behind the house. They were playing with a ball, tossing it from one to the other, running and leaping, and Deirdre was happy and radiant with joy. From the wood beyond came three youths, tall, supple, handsome of appearance and bearing, with hair black and glossy as the raven's wing. One was taller by a head than his companions. Deirdre remembered what the huntsman had told her about the three sons of Usnach — Naoise, Aillean, and Ardan — who would be glad to see her beauty. They looked at her now, but they did not stop. Deirdre left her women and ran after them, swiftly, lightly. At her first sight of Naoise her whole heart went out to him. She knew that there was no other man she could marry.

Aillean and Ardan hastened their step, bidding Naoise do likewise for they had far to go. They walked with great strides, but still Deirdre ran after them, lightly, swiftly, calling out:

"Naoise, son of Usnach, will you not wait for me?" He heard the sound as if it were far off.

"What is that call?" he asked his brothers.

"It is only the ducks on the loch", they answered. "Let us make speed, for we have far to go before dark."

Again Deirdre, running swiftly, called out:

"Naoise, son of Usnach, why do you leave me?"

"I hear a call", said Naoise.

"It is but the call of a grey goose overhead", his brothers told him. "Hasten now, for it grows dark."

A third time Deirdre called out:

"Naoise, son of Usnach, are you going away from me?"

"I hear a cry, and it is a cry of great distress", Naoise told his brothers.

"It is only the cry of the swans on the loch", they said.

"It is not that, nor the cry of the grey goose, nor of the ducks. It is a cry of distress. I hear it and I must answer, for I am under a vow and bond to answer any such cry."

Naoise turned and walked back; his brothers waited. When he saw Deirdre running towards him swiftly, lightly, he lost his whole heart to her irrevocably. They looked at each other with the eyes of love. Naoise knew that never could he leave her. This was his true love, his bride; even though he remembered what he had heard, that she was the queen-to-be of Conachur the king, his own cousin.

They kissed each other three times, Naoise and Deirdre; they walked to meet Aillean and Ardan, and Deirdre kissed them each once. Then Naoise lifted her on his shoulder and they went on together, swiftly, swiftly, until they came to the sea where the three sons of Usnach had their galley. They stepped in, and set off eastwards to Alba. There they went to Loch Etive where they built a strong tower for their dwelling, and there they lived in peace and happiness; for Aillean and Ardan came to love Deirdre as their sister.

They were great hunters and fishers, the three sons of Usnach; they caught salmon in the pool, they tracked down the deer on the hill. Deirdre gathered fruit from the trees and bushes, and there was nothing more that they desired.

But in Erin, Conachur was in great wrath. He was told of

Deirdre's flight after the three young men, whom he knew to be the sons of Usnach. He knew, too, where they had fled, for they had come and gone many a year between Erin and Alba. Now he vowed to send after them, to bring them back, to take vengeance on the three men and to make Deirdre his queen.

But on second thoughts he had a better plan. Why should he go to the trouble of sending warriors to Alba? No, he would entice the fugitives to return. So he sent messengers to all his people of Ulster bidding them to a feast, his wedding feast. Then he summoned his kinsman Fergus with his three sons, bidding them cross to Alba, to find Deirdre and the sons of Usnach, and invite them to this feast, saying nothing of his resolve to wed Deirdre. It was to be a feast of friendship, of reconciliation.

"Say to Naoise and his brothers that there can be no feast, no rejoicing at all for me unless they, my kinsmen, are present."

Fergus and his sons sailed across to Alba. They heard news of Naoise and his brothers, they followed the trail, they came to Loch Etive and the tower where they dwelt with Deirdre. There were courteous greetings between them, and a welcome for Fergus and his sons. Then Fergus delivered the message from Conachur; that he would not begin the wedding feast until Naoise and his brothers had come.

"He has sent me in friendship", Fergus declared. "And my sons and I are surety for your safety."

"I shall go", said Naoise. "And I", said Aillean. "And I too", said Ardan.

But Deirdre was reluctant. She feared the king; she would not trust his word.

"Better our own home here than any we may be given in Erin. Better our supper together in our own tower than any feast of Conachur's."

"Better to each man his own country", replied Fergus. "None can be happy away from his own place; and the country of Naoise and Aillean and Ardan is Erin".

"That is true", agreed Naoise. "Yet I have had a greater happiness here than I ever enjoyed in Erin."

"You may come safely", Fergus promised. "My sons and I are surety for you."

"I shall go with you", said Naoise again; and Aillean and Ardan after him.

"Do not go", implored Deirdre. She sang a sad song:

"I see Naoise and Aillean and Ardan without help, without defence, I see Fergus faithless, I see Conachur pitiless, without compassion, vengeful, thirsting for blood. I see three brothers laid upon the cold earth; I see Deirdre in sorrow and tears."

Fergus laughed.

"Never listen, Naoise, to the howling of dogs, or the dreams and visions of women. It will be unfriendly indeed if you do not return the friendship of Conachur, if you refuse to come to the feast."

"I shall come", said Naoise. "And I", said Aillean. "And I too", said Ardan.

Deirdre again sang a warning, her vision:

"I see three white doves with three drops of honey in their mouths. What does that mean, Naoise?"

"It is only a dream, in broken sleep, only a woman's madness, Deirdre."

"Now I see three fierce hawks with three drops of blood in their mouths. What does that mean, Naoise?"

"It is only the melancholy dream of broken sleep, Deirdre."

"I see three black ravens with three leaves from the yew, the tree of death. What does that mean, Naoise?"

"It is only the blackness of broken sleep and dreams, Deirdre. As Conachur has bidden us in friendship to come to his feast, so in friendship we must go."

"Let us indeed go now", said Fergus. "If Conachur welcomes you in friendship, all is well. If he is hostile, then my sons and I shall be with you."

"We shall indeed", his three sons agreed.

They went then, all of them together, Deirdre weeping and singing her sad farewell.

"Beloved is that land, that yonder land
Alba, full of woods and full of lochs;
Sore is my heart at leaving thee;
But I go with Naoise."

So they came again to Erin, and Fergus sent word to

Conachur, so that they might be well received. Conachur answered that he had not expected them so soon; their house was not ready for them; but their was another that they might use until their own was in order.

Naoise was not well pleased. Had not Conachur bidden them to a feast, had he not looked for their coming, had he not had a lodging prepared? He went with Deirdre and his brothers to the house where Fergus was now bidden to take them. It was full of mercenaries, who, when they saw Naoise with Deirdre and his brothers, shouted with coarse laughter. Naoise laughed louder than they did. Their captain barred the door; Naoise barred it again with two bars.

"And who are you, brave hero, who laughs so loud and who doubly bars the door?"

"I shall tell you", answered Naoise, "if you will tell me why you laughed and why you barred the door."

"I shall tell you indeed", roared the captain. "Never have I seen men coming here whose blood I so desire to shed as yours. Now why, great hero, did *you* laugh?"

"I shall tell you", said Naoise. "Never have I seen any man, living or dead, whom I so desired to slay, not one in the whole wide world."

He caught the captain, while Aillean and Ardan each seized another man; their strength was as great as their wrath, and it was not long before they had killed all those mercenaries. They threw out the bodies, they cleaned the house and lit a bright fire, and sheltered and slept there until dawn.

Meanwhile Conachur, who had made that vile plot and laid that cruel snare, was waiting for news of the death of the three brothers, and of Deidre's being his for the taking.

"Go down to the house of the mercenaries", he told Lavarcham, and bring me news of Deirdre. If she is as beautiful as she was, I shall make her my queen. If not, then Naoise (if he is still alive) may have her."

Lavarcham went down to the house. She crouched on the ground and peered through the chicken-hole in the door, then came back to the king.

"Alas, all her beauty is faded and gone", she told him.

"I shall have another account of that", said the king, and

he sent one of his men; who, like Lavarcham, crouched down and peered through the chicken-hole in the door. He saw Deirdre, who blushed deeply, knowing quite well that someone was spying on her. Naoise saw the blush, and knew that it meant that someone was looking at Deirdre. They were playing a game with dice, and he threw one of the dice at the hole in the door. It struck the eye of the man peering in and blinded him.

"You went off cheerfully", Conachur greeted him, "and now you return dolefully. What has happened? Have you seen Deirdre?"

"I saw her, but only for a moment. Then Naoise threw a dice at me and blinded me. But such is her beauty that had you not bidden me hasten back I would have stayed to look on her with my other eye."

"So — I believe you", the king told him. "Now let three hundred warriors go and seize her and bring her here; and let them kill the three sons of Usnach."

"The hunt is coming", Deirdre told Naoise.

"I shall go and slay them", he declared.

Now the three sons of Fergus had come to that house with Naoise and his brothers, and the eldest said:

"You will not go. I will go myself, for I have sworn to be your surety."

He went out and slew a third of the men. Conachur came out of his palace to see what had happened. He looked down and saw the son of Fergus slaying his men.

"Cease this work, son of Fergus", he called. "And I will give you land for yourself, for your father and for your grandfather."

The man paused, listened, and went over to the king.

"He has gone; he will not come back to us", Deirdre told Naoise.

"Yet he has done good work", said Naoise.

"I shall go now and take his place", said the second son. He went out and slew another third of the men. Conachur came too look down:

"Who are you who are slaying my men?"

"I am the second son of Fergus."

"Give over then, and come to my side. You shall have

land for yourself, for your father and for your grandfather."

The second son went over to the king.

"He has gone; he will not come back", said Deirdre to Naoise.

"Yet he has done good work", answered Naoise.

"I shall go now, and I shall not go over to Conachur", vowed the third son. So he went out and began slaying the foemen as his brothers had done.

Conachur looked down from his palace.

"Who are you who are slaying my men?"

"I am the third son of Fergus."

"Come over to me and I shall give you land for yourself, and your father and your grandfather, as I have given to your brothers."

"I shall not come over to you", answered the brave and loyal youth. "But I shall go to my father and tell him what you have done to your kinsmen Naoise and his brothers."

He went into the house again and told Naoise.

"Your enemies are slain. Now I must go to my father and tell him of Conachur's treachery. But now you are safe from him and his warriors."

"Go, with out thanks and blessing", Naoise told him, and he went away; and of what passed between him and his father, the false-hearted Fergus, and his brothers, it has not been told.

It was dawn now, and Naoise said to Deirdre and his brothers:

"Let us go now, back to the sea and our galley, and sail again for Alba; and never return to Erin."

They went away, walking swiftly. But Conachur had not finished with them. He sent for his arch-druid and commanded him to work a spell.

"I shall turn back the sons of Usnach", promised the druid.

He raised a dark wood before them, but they went through.

"You have done no good, and they have taken no harm", Conachur said in wrath.

"I shall put a deep grey sea in front of them, so that they will not be able to pass."

The druid flooded the way with a grey sea, but Naoise put

Deirdre on his shoulder, and he and his brothers waded through the deeps.

"You have done no good, they have taken no harm", said Conachur in bitter wrath. "Of what use is your magic?"

"I shall put the sea in front of them again, and turn it to ice. The waves will be like great crags."

He cast his evil spell, and in front of Naoise and his brothers was a sea of frozen waves, great icy crags as sharp as swords. They halted; they could go no further.

"Come up upon my shoulder", Naoise told Ardan. "I can carry you too."

Ardan obeyed; but he was chilled and weary to death, and death took him.

Then Aillean said:

"Leave me here, for death is upon me, and I must not hold you back."

"I will not leave you", said Naoise. "Come up on my shoulder, for I can carry you too."

Aillean climbed on that broad shoulder; but all the strength was gone from him, and he died. When Naoise saw that both his brothers were dead, all his strength, all his desire for life drained from him and he was with them in death.

"They are all gone now, the three of them", the druid told Conachur, "and will not trouble you again. I have done what you bade me; Deirdre is there now for your taking."

"You have done well", Conachur told him, "and you shall have your reward. Now bid the ice melt and the sea withdraw, and I shall have Deirdre."

The druid obeyed. The great sharp crags melted, the grey sea withdrew, and he saw the three brothers lying on the green machair, held in death, and Deirdre bending sadly over them.

Conachur ordered that a deep grave be dug. That was done, and the three sons of Usnach were laid in it. Deirdre stood on the green machair and looked on. She did not weep, she spoke only to the dead:

"Move now Naoise, and lie close to Aillean and to Ardan. If the dead can hear — move and make room for me."

She leaped down into the grave and lay close by Naoise, and death was upon her as on him and his brothers.

But the evil king's vengeance was not finished, his

jealousy not sated. He ordered her body to be taken from that grave and buried in another grave on the other side of the loch, and this was done. But an immense pine tree grew from her grave, and another one from the grave of the three brothers, and the two pines grew towards each other and intertwined across the waters of the loch.

Conachur ordered them to be cut down. They grew again, and again he had them cut down. They grew and intertwined a third time, and a third time he ordered them to be cut down.

There came a time when he married a young queen who was compassionate and gentle, such a wife as he did not deserve. And she persuaded or compelled him to leave the two trees intertwined across the waters, as had been the loves of Deirdre and Naoise in their life together.

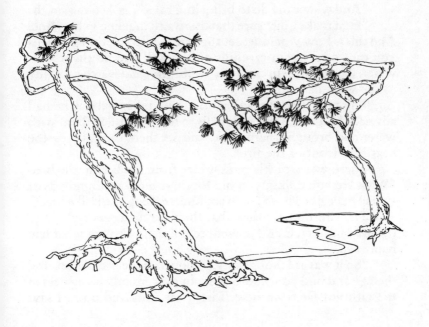

The Smith and the Fairies

There was a smith once whose name was MacEachern. His wife had died, and he had one child, a son, who was his comfort and delight. This boy had never given him any anxiety; he was healthy and sturdy, lively and good-tempered, and already showed the makings of a good craftsman like his father. But one day, quite suddenly, he fell ill, from no cause that could be found, and no sort of illness that could be easily recognised and cured. He simply took to his bed, and lay there without making any effort to get up, and failed to respond in any way to his father's care and anxiety. He grew thinner and thinner, although he ate enough for three.

One day an old man walked into the smithy, where MacEachern was at work by himself. He was a wise old man whom the smith knew and greatly respected, so he told him all his trouble.

"It is not your son who lies there", the wise old man told him. "It is a changeling. The Other People have taken away your boy, to work for them".

"And what can I do to bring him back?", asked the smith.

"First make quite sure that this *is* a changeling in his place. And this is how you must set about it. Collect all the egg shells you can, carry them carefully to the well and fill them with water. Then lay them carefully by the fire, and watch carefully to see what happens."

The poor father thanked him and did exactly as he had advised. He carried the egg shells to the well, filled them with water and brought them back, and set them carefully on the hearth in front of the fire.

There was a cackle of laughter from the boy in the bed. "What are you doing, you old fool? Never in the hundreds of years I have lived have I seen anyone treat egg shells like that."

The smith knew then that the wise man was right, and this *was* a changeling. He went to tell the wise man what had happened.

"So it was as I thought. Now you must get rid of him, and then go and find your son who is almost certainly being held in the rath not far from here. Listen carefully and do as I say.

Build a great fire on the hearth, seize the changeling, and throw him in."

MacEachern went home and did as he was told. The fire blazed up: "What is that for?", demanded the creature in the bed.

"You'll soon see", answered the smith. He seized the changeling, and threw him into the fire; with a wild yell the creature leaped up and out through the smoke hole in the roof, and that was the last seen or heard of him.

The smith went back to the wise man to thank him.

"Now you are free to go to the rath and find your son. A night is coming very soon when you will see the rath lit up with bright lights, the door open, and sweet music coming from within. Walk to the door carrying with you your Bible, a cock, and a dirk. Walk straight into the green mound, but first stick the dirk in the threshold so that the door cannot close.

You will find yourself in a splendid hall, full of the Little People dancing to the music. At the further end you will see your son, working at an anvil. The Little People will welcome you and ask what you want. Tell them you want only your son, and that you will not go without him."

A night or two later, the smith saw the fairy mound brilliant with light, and heard sweet music coming from it. He walked there, his Bible hidden under his coat, the cock asleep under his arm, the dirk in his hand. He felt desperately afraid — but he trusted the word of the wise man, and he trusted the protection of the Word of God. So he walked steadily into the rath, having thrust his dirk into the threshold.

Within the fairy mound he saw a great company, richly dressed, all whirling and dancing to the music. At the far end he saw his son, working at an anvil. The music stopped, and some of the Little People came towards him. They greeted him politely:

"What will you have? A glass of wine?"

"I want only my son, and I will not go without him", the smith told them. They gave a great shout of mocking laughter. This awoke the cock, who began to crow loudly. The people shrieked with fear and rage, they seized the boy and thrust him and his father out of the rath. As he crossed the threshold the smith pulled his dirk out of the ground, the door clanged shut, and once more the mound was dark and silent.

The boy walked home with his father. He was very quiet, but he appeared to be quite well. He ate his supper, and went to bed; next day and the next he was silent and idle; his father was very patient.

He waited many days, he waited a whole year. The boy was good and biddable, but he took no part in the work of the smithy. Then one day the smith was working on a fine sword, ordered by a gentleman in the neighbourhood. The boy, who was with him looking on, suddenly exclaimed: "That is not the way to do it. Let me show you."

He pushed his father aside, stood by the anvil and finished making the sword. "Now you see how it is done."

Indeed it was a splendid piece of craftsmanship, a more magnificent sword than anyone had seen before. The gentleman was delighted, and brought his friends. The son taught his father the new way, and invented his own kind of sword. In time he grew up and married and had sons of his own. They were all fine craftsmen like their father and grandfather, and they in turn passed on their talent.

So the MacEacherns lived in peace and comfort for many generations, greatly honoured in the neighbourhood. And never a one of them went back to the fairy mound.

The White Pet

There was a farmer once who had a fine sheep with a light and soft fleece, called The White Pet. This sheep lived very peacefully at pasture and in the fold, until one day she heard the farmer and his wife talking about Christmas which was coming near, and about their provisions and preparations.

"I'd better be killing The White Pet before she grows old and tough", said the farmer. "She'll make good tender eating now."

His wife agreed:

"We'll have joints and chops, and I'll make some pies."

The White Pet did not like that idea at all, so off she went, out of the farm, along a bit of road, and across a field. There she met a bull who said:

"Good day to you, and where are you off to?"

"Anywhere in the wide world but here", the sheep told

33

him. "They are planning to kill me for Christmas, so it is better to be away."

"Indeed and it is", agreed the bull. "Will you let me come with you? I am not at all sure that I am to be spared much longer."

"You are welcome", White Pet told him politely, and on they went together. Presently they met a dog.

"Good day to you both", he greeted them.

"Good day to yourself", they replied.

"And where are you off to?"

"Anywhere but here. We are both to be killed for Christmas, so it is time to be leaving."

"Will you let me come with you?", asked the dog. "I don't like the looks I've been having from my master, it may be that he thinks I'm too old, and wants a young dog who can work harder. I would'nt put it past him to be killing me."

"Then come with us and welcome", the two travellers told him.

Next they met a cat.

"Good day to you", said the cat politely.

"Good day to you", they replied together.

"And where does your journey take you?"

"Och it does not much matter so long as it is far enough from here. We have all heard our masters talk of killing us before Christmas."

"Well I wouldn't trust my master very far either", said the cat. "Will you let me come with you?"

"Surely; come along."

The dog and the cat looked at each other, and decided to make friends.

"Cats aren't all bad", thought the dog. "This one looks harmless enough."

"There are *some* decent dogs", the cat said to herself.

Before long they met a fine fat goose.

"Whither away?" she asked.

"Well away from here", White Pet answered for them all. "We've all heard our masters talk of killing us."

"I know mine is going to", said the goose. "He said to my mistress that a roast goose would be fine for Christmas dinner."

"Then you'd better come along with us", White Pet told the goose, who was very pleased to join them.

Finally they met a cock who crowed at them in a friendly way. He too was likely to be killed for Christmas, and he too was very thankful to be asked to join them.

All that day they went steadily on. Darkness was falling and they were anxious to find shelter for the night.

Not far ahead they saw a light, and they went towards it, and found that it came from the window of a cottage. They looked in at the window and saw a band of thieves sitting on the floor counting their money.

"Now let us each make his own call", said White Pet. "Baa-aa-aa." She said it loudly.

At the same moment the bull gave a great bellow; the dog barked furiously, the cat squalled, the goose screeched, and the cock crew more loudly than he had ever crowed before.

It was startling enough to make the robbers leap up and run for their lives out of the cottage, leaving their treasure behind. They ran without looking about them, and did not see the company at the window.

So these tired travellers went in and settled themselves. There was plenty of room for all. The White Pet took charge of the sleeping arrangements, and made sure of their comfort.

The cock flew up to the rafters, the cat went into a cupboard, the goose went outside again to the midden, the dog lay on the hearth, the bull behind the door, White Pet in the middle of the floor. All was still, and they were nearly asleep when one of the robbers came creeping back. He thought he might recover the treasure. There would be candles in the cupboard, and he would light one and look for it.

But when he put his hand into the cupboard the cat dug her claws into it. All the same, he took out a candle and went to the fire to light it. There was a pot of water standing on the hearth; the dog rose, put his tail into the water and shook it, which put out the candle.

"There's a witch or a warlock or the devil himself in this house", said the thief to himself, and he ran for the door. But he fell over the sheep who gave him a kick, and bumped into the bull who butted him hard; and when he rushed out of the door the goose began beating him on the legs with her wings.

He ran back to the wood where his comrades were waiting. "How did you get on?" they asked him.

"Not too well; not well at all", he told them.

"First, there was a man hiding in the cupboard where I went for a candle, and he thrust sharp knives into my hand. Then after I lit the candle a black man by the fire sprinkled water on it and put it out. I made for the door, but a man in the middle of the floor gave me a push and a kick, and I had another violent blow from another man at the door itself. And when I came out there was a cobbler who beat me about the legs with his apron and I nearly fell. So I'm not going back there, for any money."

"We'd better not go either", the rest of the band agreed.

So that night and for all the nights and days to come White Pet and her companions, the bull and the dog, the cat, the goose and the cock were left in peace, so they just settled down and lived happily together.

The King of Lochlann's three Daughters

The King of Lochlann had three daughters, all of them beautiful, happy, and well loved. One day they went walking and did not return. Three giants had seized them and carried them away. The king had searchers sent out, searching in the woods, on the hills and valleys, but never a trace of the vanished girls could they find. Then he consulted a wise man.

"I can tell you where they are", the wise man said. "They are in the kingdom of the giants deep under the earth."

"And how can they be rescued?"

"Only by a man who can build a ship that will sail on land as well as on water."

"Well, if such a man is found, and if he rescues my daughters, he may have the eldest for his wife, and be my heir", declared the king. And he had this proclamation made throughout his kingdom. It came to the hearing of the three sons of a poor widow, who lived a long way off.

"There's my chance", said the eldest to himself, and he asked his mother:

37

"Will you bake me a bannock, and I'll be away to find my fortune?"

"Will you have a little bannock with my blessing, or a big bannock without it?"

"Och, never mind the blessing, I'll need every bit of a big bannock."

His mother did as he asked, and her son went off to a wood by a river, and began cutting down a tree to build a ship. When he felt tired he sat down and began to eat his bannock. A water-sprite came up out of the river and begged:

"Will you give me a bit of your bannock?"

"I will not; I want it all myself."

The water-sprite went back into the river, and the man went back to his wood-cutting. But as soon as he cut off a branch it grew again, as soon as he cut down a tree it took root again, till at last he gave up and went home.

"How did you get on?", they asked him, but he only growled at them and went to bed.

Next morning the second son asked his mother:

"Will you bake me a bannock, and I'll be off to find my fortune?" "Will you have a little bannock with my blessing, or a big one without it?"

"Och, what do I want with a blessing? I want a big bannock."

So his mother baked a fine big bannock, and he put it in his pouch and went off, without even bothering to thank her. He came to the wood by the river, he began cutting down a tree; when he felt tired he sat down to eat his bannock, and the water-sprite came up out of the river and asked;

"Will you give me a bit of your bannock?"

"Why should I? There isn't enough for two, and I'll want it all myself."

The water-sprite went back under the river, and the man went back to his wood-cutting. But every branch he cut grew again, every tree he cut down took root again, till at last he gave it up and went home. When they asked him how he had got on, he was surly and told them nothing.

Next morning the third son asked his mother:

"Please will you bake me a bannock, and I'll be off to find my fortune."

"Will you have a little bannock with my blessing, or a big one without it?"

"I wouldn't like to be going off without your blessing. A little bannock will do very well, thank you."

So he had the bannock with his mother's blessing, and he thanked her and went off to the wood. There he began cutting down a tree, and when he felt tired he sat down to eat his bannock. No sooner had he started to eat than the water-sprite came up out of the river.

"Will you give me a bit of your bannock?"

"I will, and gladly. It's a good bannock."

He gave the water-sprite half of his bannock. She thanked him and said:

"Don't you be tiring yourself with any more wood-cutting. I know what you want. Go home now and come back in a year and a day, and you'll find your ship ready."

The lad thanked her, she went back to the river, and he went home.

When they asked how he had got on he said:

"Och, fine", but told them no more. For a year and a day he stayed at home, then he went back to the wood, and there on the river he saw floating a fine ship. He went aboard, called out his thanks to the water-sprite and sailed off down the river. He had not sailed far before he saw a man kneeling on the bank, bending down and drinking great gulps of water.

"What are you doing?" "I'm having a good drink. It takes a river to give me enough water for my thirst."

"Come along with me. We may be of service to each other, and you may find something better to drink than water."

The man came aboard. They sailed off the river, across a bit of land, and came upon a man eating a young ox.

"And what are you doing?", asked the lad.

"I'm having a bite of meat. It takes all this to satisfy my hunger."

"Come along with me. We may help each other to find our fortunes, and you'll have better to eat than raw meat."

The man jumped on board. Presently they saw another man kneeling with his ear to the ground.

"And what are you doing?", called the lad.

"I'm listening to the grass growing. I can hear a great deal of what is happening under the earth."

"Come along with us and we shall help each other to find our fortunes."

The third man came aboard. The lad told them the quest he was on, and the third man said:

"You can get off the ship now, for I can hear the giants down below the earth here."

So they all disembarked and came to a great deep hole in the ground. Beside it lay a great creel with a rope round a big rock.

"We can let ourselves down in that creel", said the listening man, and down they went, two at a time.

They heard a roar and found a huge giant glaring at them.

"Who are you and where are you going? If you are after rescuing the princesses, one of you will have to drink as much as I do, or I'll kill the lot of you."

"Is there a river here?", asked the first man, the drinker.

"There is, and I'll take you there."

The two of them, the man and the giant, knelt down and began drinking, but before the man had drunk enough the giant was bloated and dead.

They went on a bit further, and were met by another giant.

"Who are you and where are you going? Do you think you can carry off the princesses?", he roared at them. "One of you will first have to eat as much as I do, or I'll kill the lot of you."

"Have you an ox or two?", asked the second man, the eater.

"I have, and I'll take you to them."

The man and the giant began eating a young ox, but before the man was satisfied, the giant was dead with overeating. So the three men and the lad walked on a bit further, till they met the third giant. He had more sense than his brothers, and was perhaps better-natured too, although that wouldn't be saying much.

"You'll be after the princesses", he roared at them. "Well I don't want to be risking my life, and you don't want to be risking yours. I have a proposal to make to you, young fellow", he said to the lad, the widow's son. "If you will undertake to serve me for a year and a day, I'll allow your three friends to take the girls back to their father. How does this strike you?"

The lad promised to serve him for a year and a day, and the three men gladly agreed to take the princesses back to their father. So the three princesses were released, and the young fellow made his three friends promise to tell the king the whole story, and that he would be coming back at the end of a year and a day.

"We shall", the men promised. They were sent up, two by two in the creel. But when they came out at the top, the men began plotting together. They put the fear of death in the princesses, and warned them not to tell their father anything about the lad, their true rescuer. The eldest princess murmured to her sisters:

"Let us say we'll marry them in a year and a day."

So they all came to the palace, and the king was overwhelmed with joy. He welcomed the three men, each of whom asked for a princess in marriage; the girls begged for the delay of a year and a day, and this was readily agreed.

Down in the giant's land the lad served his master faithfully, and at the end of his time the giant said:

"You've done well and I'll let you go. And I'll whistle for my eagle to carry you up and out."

The eagle came swooping down. The lad mounted, and the giant gave him a load of meat. "The eagle will be needing all that for the journey."

As they flew, the eagle kept turning her beak for food, and before they had reached the landing place the meat was all finished. The lad cut a piece from his own thigh and fed her. When she swooped to earth, near the king's palace, she said:

"You've been kind to me and I'll be helpful to you. Take this whistle, and any time you need help, just blow it and I'll come. And now good luck be with you."

"And with you too; and my best thanks", said the lad.

He walked to the town where the palace stood, and found a smith. He asked him if he wanted a servant to blow the bellows and do any other work for him. The smith did need help, and the lad set to work at once. There were great doings in the palace and in the town, the smith told him, for the king's three daughters were to be married to the three champions who had rescued them from the giants. It was rumoured that the princesses were not entirely happy about this arrangement, but the king had given a promise and he would have to keep it.

At that moment a messenger from the palace came to summon the smith. Not long afterwards, he returned from the palace looking shaken and dismayed.

"What is the matter?", asked his wife, and he told her: "The king's eldest daughter has commanded me to make her a golden crown exactly like the one she had in the giant's house. And how can I tell what it was like?"

The lad, who was listening, begged to be allowed to try his hand. The smith gave him the gold, the lad shut himself in the smithy, and began blowing up the fire; but he did not melt the gold. He cut it up into little pieces and threw them out of the window. When all the people outside were scrambling to pick up the bits, he blew his whistle, and the eagle came swooping in at the window: "What will you have me do?"

"Can you bring me the golden crown which the eldest princess had in the giant's house?" "I can and I will." In no time at all she was back with a beautiful golden crown. The lad took it to his master, who was amazed and grateful; he went straight to the palace.

His triumph was short-lived, for he came back from the palace looking quite cast down.

"What ails you?", asked his wife. "Was the princess not pleased?" "She was indeed; but her sister, the second daughter, says I must make her a silver crown exactly like the one she had in the giant's house, and I don't know at all what it is like."

"Now don't be distressing yourself." the lad told him. "Give me the silver and leave me alone in the forge."

Again he shut himself in, blew up the fire, and cut the silver into little pieces which he threw out of the window. Again he blew his whistle, and again the eagle came flying in.

"What will you have me do?" "Will you bring me the silver crown from the giant's house?" "I will, in no time at all" — and she did.

The lad gave the crown to his master, who gave him great praise and thanks, and took the crown up to the palace. Again he came back looking very far from happy.

"What did they say to you?", asked his wife. "Were they not well pleased?" The second princess was, but her youngest sister now demands a copper crown just like the one she had in the giant's house."

"Well, let me try my hand again," said the lad. And for a third time he shut himself into the smithy, blew up the fire, cut up the copper, and threw it all out of the window. For the third time he blew his whistle and the faithful eagle came. He asked her if she could bring him the copper crown. "Of course I can" — and she did, and he gave it to his master, who took it to the palace. There he was thanked profusely by the princesses, and indeed by the king himself.

"You've done well, and you must have your reward."

The smith was an honest man.

"It was not I who made the crowns, my lord. It was my servant, and it is he who should have the reward."

"I'll send for him", said the king. He ordered a coach to be driven to the smithy, with two grooms in attendance, to bring the lad. The grooms found him busy, and all black and dirty with soot from the forge. They mocked him and seized him, and threw him like a bundle of rubbish into the coach. As it drove off, the lad blew his whistle. The eagle swooped down and into the coach, unseen by the coachman or the grooms.

"What can I do for you this time?" "Let me out of this, and fill the coach with stones." "That is easy enough", said the eagle. The lad went back to the forge, and the coach was driven to the palace, where the king was at the door. When he saw the coach full of stones he was in a great rage at this insult, and he ordered the grooms to be thrashed and thrown into a dungeon. Then he sent the coach back to the smithy with other two grooms. But they were no better. They too mocked the lad, threw him into the coach, and slammed the door on him.

Again, he blew his whistle, again the eagle came and let him out, and filled the coach with piles of dirt. The lad went quietly back to the smithy and his work.

When the king saw the coach full of dirt he was more furious than ever, and had the grooms thrashed and thrown into a dungeon.

For the third time he sent the coach, but this time put his

own servant in charge, a decent, civil man who spoke courteously to the lad.

"The king bids me to bring you to him, but you'll want to clean yourself up a bit first. I'll wait for you."

When the lad came out, clean and tidy (though shabby in his dress) the footman led him by the hand, showed him into the coach, bowed as if to a fine gentleman, and shut the door gently. As they drove off, the lad blew his whistle and the eagle came, but this time she was not asked to let him out.

Will you bring me that suit of gold and silver cloth that lies in the giant's house?" begged the youth. "I will, and gladly." In no time at all she had brought the fine suit, the lad changed into it, and when the king's footman opened the door for him at the palace, out stepped a handsome gentleman in a fine suit.

The king gave him a great welcome, and the three princesses were more than delighted to see him again. They told the king the true story of their rescue from the giants, and revealed the three false friends as shameless liars. The eldest princess had a particular sparkle in her eyes as she welcomed the young fellow to the palace.

The king sent for the three false comrades to be brought to him for punishment, and there is no doubt that this would have been severe. But they had been given warning, and by this time they were far away. It was really not worth pursuing them.

The king ordered a magnificent feast to be prepared. "I am glad to give you my eldest daughter as bride, and to proclaim you as my heir", he told the good lad. The wedding was arranged, and there was great rejoicing throughout the land. The kind lad begged that the good smith and his wife be bidden as guests of honour, and that the smith be rewarded as if he had made the three crowns himself. This was willingly granted by the king.

The tale says nothing about what happened to the hero's two surly brothers. But he did send for his good mother, bidding her to come and give him her blessing; and he told her there was no need to bother making a bannock for the occasion.

Grania and Diarmid

Fionn, the great hero of Erin and Alba, had a band of warriors and comrades who nearly matched him in strength, and who followed him with loyalty. Chief among them, and dearly loved by Fionn, was Diarmid his nephew; the most handsome of all that band. Not only was he handsome, tall and broad, and swift in movement, but he had on his forehead a love-spot which compelled every woman who looked on him to fall in love with him: young women, matrons, old women. They would not leave him alone, but followed him to the hunt, and on all the journeys, sports, forayings, and expeditions of the Fianna. His comrades complained and went on complaining, not without cause. They were not jealous, but a woman is a nuisance on such excursions, and it was not one woman, nor even two or three, but a whole troop of them.

So Diarmid, who did not want the women any more than his comrades did, had a little cap made to fit closely over his forehead and hide the love-spot. The women left him in peace, and all went well until one day a little dog leapt up at him, begging to be caressed. Diarmid bent down, patted and fondled the dog, and his cap fell off, showing the love-spot. Only one woman was there to see it; but she was the most important woman of all, Grania, the wife of Fionn himself.

45

She was among the most beautiful of women and many men had desired her, but when she spoke to Diarmid bidding him come with her, leaving Fionn, leaving Erin, he naturally refused, for he was loyal.

"I will not go with you, I will not betray Fionn, you are his bride and you are for no other man."

Then she put three spells upon him, for she had learned some magic from her nurse: a spell upon his eyes that he might see what she wished him to see; a spell upon his tongue to make him say what she wished him to say; a spell upon his heart to compel him to love her.

And it came about that profoundly as she loved him, he loved her no less and could no longer resist her. He saw her as she wished him to see her, he spoke the words she desired to hear.

"I will go with you, Grania." His heart and will were hers. "We must leave Erin; we must sail to Alba", he told her, and she went gladly with him. They sailed across the sea eastward to Alba. There they came to a green glen, where Diarmid built a wooden hut for their dwelling. He was skilled in carpentry and he made wooden bowls, sitting by the river as he worked. The shavings fell into the stream and floated downstream.

Now Fionn had discovered their flight, and set out to follow them with his men, in great wrath. They too sailed to Alba, and they followed first one path, then another; one day they sat down to rest by a stream, and there they saw the shavings of wood floating downstream.

"These come from some work of Diarmid's", declared Fionn. "We are on his track, let us go upstream until we find him."

They walked upstream and came to the dwelling of Diarmid and Grania. Very craftily, Fionn hid his rage and jealousy, and called to Diarmid.

"We have come to you, we want you with us on our hunt. It is not the stag we are hunting, but the great boar, the poison-boar, that is ravaging this countryside and killing many. We must hunt him to death, and we need your skill, Diarmid."

Diarmid too had heard of that boar with the poison-bristles. He loved the hunt, and he had not lost his love for Fionn and his comrades. He went with them gladly, although Grania begged him not to go. She had no trust in Fionn, she saw only darkness and sorrow.

They hunted all that day, and the next, and on the third day they came upon the boar, huge and fierce and terrible. It was Fionn who killed him, and there was great rejoicing.

"How large is he?", asked Fionn. "I have heard that he is four times seven feet."

"And I have heard it is three times seven feet", said Diarmid.

"You may be right — but I think I am", said Fionn. "But let us measure him."

Diarmid measured the dead boar, stretching his arms wide. He measured along the bristles, not touching them.

"It is three times seven feet", he announced.

"Is it so? I could have sworn it was four times seven. Will you measure him again, close against the bristles", Fionn bade him.

Diarmid obeyed. One of the poisoned bristles pierced his arm and he fell, dying, to the ground.

"Help me, Fionn", he implored. "Let me drink water from your healing cup that you carry. There is a well not far from here."

Fionn had indeed this wonderful cup. Whatever was drunk from it would drive out poison and make a sick or a dying man well.

"I do not have the cup with me", he told Diarmid. "But the well is very near. Its waters are healing and I shall bring you some in my two hands, and you will be cured."

He went to the well and filled his cupped hands with the pure water. Then he remembered Diarmid's sin against him, and his wrath and bitterness grew. "I will not take the healing water to him; I will let him die." He loosed his hands and the water drained into the ground.

"Where is the healing water?", asked Diarmid when Fionn came back. "I am dying of thirst."

Then Fionn's anger left him, and he was filled with compassion.

"I'll go again, and this time I shall be careful not to spill a single drop", he promised as he went off, and again he filled his cupped hands, and began to return; but again bitter anger and jealousy overcame him and he spilled the water.

"Where is the water. Let me drink", implored Diarmid. "I am very near death."

The heart of Fionn was drained of bitterness and filled with compassion and grief. He ran to the well, filled his cupped hands with the water, and ran back to Diarmid without spilling a single drop. He had never run so swiftly in his life, but swift as he was, death was swifter and had taken Diarmid.

Silently, in grief and shame, the Fianna carried his body back to Grania. They dug a grave for him there, where the lovers had dwelt together.

Grania stood watching, in silence. As they laid Diarmid in the grave she uttered a lament; and then, before they could lay one piece of earth, one single turf upon his body, she leapt into the deep grave and lay beside him. Death came upon her too.

So earth was piled upon them both, and they were left there together, Grania and Diarmid; and Fionna and the Fianna returned to Erin.

The Knight of the Riddles

There was once a king who was married very happily to a good and gentle queen. She bore him a son, but in child-bearing she died, and the king was broken-hearted. For a time he lived alone, grieving; but his people urged him to marry again, and he found a second queen. She too gave him a son, but she did not die in her child-bearing — though it would have been well if she had, for she was evil, and jealous of her step-son, and resolved to put her own son in his place.

Now there was no vestige of jealousy between her son and his elder brother; there was only great love between them, and this was very good. They grew together in joy and friendship.

The day came when the queen began to plot against her stepson. She went to the cook with poison, which she commanded him to drop into the elder prince's drinking cup at supper. The cook, who feared her, would have obeyed; but her own son overheard what was said and he told his brother, who refused the cup at supper. The queen went again to the cook; she thought the prince had drunk from his cup, but the poison had not been strong enough.

"You must use this, a stronger poison." The cook obeyed, but again her son had followed her, and overheard, and again he warned his brother. Again the prince refused his cup, but this time he said:

"It is better that I leave here. I'll take the world for my pillow, and follow where fortune leads me."

"And I will go with you", declared his young brother. So

49

early next morning they went to the stable, saddled a horse, and mounted together. The older brother had a bottle with him, into which he had poured some of the wine from his cup at supper.

"Let us see if it is still potent", he said, and poured a drop into the horse's ear. Immediately the horse dropped down dead.

"That is bad; but worse if I had drunk it myself!"

They decided to flay the horse, and use his hide as covering for the night. When they awoke in the morning they saw twelve ravens fly out of the wood where they had been sheltering. The birds began to devour the flesh of the horse, but before they had more than pecked at it they too were dead from the strong poison.

The two princes stuffed the dead birds into their saddle-bags, and walked to a town that was not far off. There they found a baker, gave him the birds and bade him bake twelve pies each filled with the flesh. When that was done they went on their way again, and by nightfall they came to a dark wood. Here they were seized by a band of twenty-four robbers, who demanded their money and any treasure they might have.

"We have no money, we have no treasure", the elder brother told them. "We are poor lads going out into the world to seek our fortune. But we have some food: twelve pies."

The robbers seized these and ate them greedily, and at once they fell down dead.

This brought no grief to the princes.

"Let's see what they had", suggested the elder. What the robbers had was a surprising amount of gold and silver. The brothers took as much as they wanted, slept safely that night, and in the morning continued their journey. At nightfall they came to the house of the Knight of the Riddles of whom they had heard much. He was a fine man, living in a beautiful big house, but the finest of all his possessions was his daughter, who was very beautiful. It was well known that the knight had a passion for asking riddles, and almost as great a liking for being asked them. So the princes asked him:

"What is the answer to this? One killed twelve: twelve killed twenty-four."

The knight could not find an answer, and invited the princes to stay as his guests until he did find one.

Before they arrived at his house, the brothers had agreed to present themselves as a traveller and his gillie or servant, the younger being the gillie. A day or two later, one of the maids who waited on the knight's daughter came and began coaxing him to tell her the answer to the riddle. He would not; instead, he took the plaid off her, and whether she liked that or not has not been told; but she went away. Another maid came, and another and another — twelve of them over twelve days; to none did he tell the answer, but from each one he took her plaid.

Finally the lady herself came to the elder brother, begging and coaxing him to tell her the answer. For a while he refused, but she was so lovely and so wheedling that at last he gave in, and told her — but then he took her plaid off her.

The lady told her father the answer, and he sent for the elder brother.

"Now I can answer your riddle", and he did so. "And now", he went on, "I give you the choice between losing your head — as many have done who came here to ask me a riddle, and who could not answer the one I asked them — and being put out to sea in a boat without oars, and without food or drink."

"Before I choose", said the prince, "I have another riddle to ask you. My gillie went out shooting one day and shot at a bird. It fell down dead, and he took off its skin and its feathers. Then he shot another and another — until he had brought down twelve, and from every one he took the skin and feathers. Then I went with him and a larger and finer bird flew above us, and I shot this one and brought it down myself, and took off its skin and feathers."

The knight of the riddles knew very well what he meant.

"Then you need not choose between losing your head, and being put to sea in a boat without oars, and without food and drink. You may marry my daughter and be my heir."

So there was a wedding with a grand feast, and it may have lasted for a day or for seven days or for twelve, nobody told me. And when it was all over, the elder prince said to the younger:

"I am well content to stay here with my wife, in this kingdom to which I am now heir; and I am happy to give up to you my share in our father's kingdom. So back you go to him, and may luck go with you."

The younger brother was grateful, and they parted with mutual goodwill. Luck went with him. His father welcomed him with joy, and heard the tale of his adventures and the good fortune of his elder brother. Of the wicked queen nothing is said — it may well be that she died of rage, and that need not grieve us.

The years passed happily for both brothers; the elder with his wife and children and father-in-law, the younger in his father's kingdom. They heard no news of each other. Then suddenly disaster threatened the kingdom of the elder brother. Just beyond its boundaries lived three cruel giants who lay in wait for travellers and wanderers, robbed and killed them, and who pillaged all the countryside and kept all the people in constant terror. It became impossible to enter or leave the kingdom without serious danger to life and limb, and the whole country lived in constant terror.

"It is high time that someone dealt with those giants", said the old knight. "What about yourself?" he asked the prince.

"Indeed I will try", agreed the latter.

He armed himself with a sharp sword and a white shield and off he went. He met the three giants and took them on in single combat, one by one; it was a fierce fight every time, and he was near death from his wounds and exhaustion. But he fought bravely and slew the three giants, one by one.

The people were nearly as mad with joy and gratitude as previously they had been with terror. They hailed their deliverer as The Knight of the White Shield; tales and ballads about his valour spread all over the country and beyond, as far as the prince's own former land. There his brother heard the tale, though he did not learn the champion's true name. He was roused to emulation, to set himself against this great warrior. So he set forth, and before long he came to the land once ruled by the three giants, and now ruled by that Knight of the White Shield, to whom he sent his challenge. This was accepted. Nothing in his journey had reminded the younger brother of that other adventure many years ago, and the two brothers met without recognising each other.

The challenge was to a wrestling match. It was such a fight as few had ever seen, for both men were strong; but the younger had just a little more strength than the elder. They paused for a moment — and suddenly the Knight of the White Shield leaped clean over the high rampart of his castle, outside which they had met and wrestled.

"Never have I seen a leap like that", said the younger to himself. The Knight of the White Shield shouted a challenge to him to renew the match in the morning, and the younger went off to find shelter for the night.

He came to a hut where he was given food and a bed, and where he slept until daylight.

In the morning the two wrestlers met again, and once again they wrestled until both were exhausted. By this time they found themselves beside the river, and the Knight of the White Shield was about to leap over the river, when a sudden thought struck him. He turned and looked at his opponent.

"I am thinking there is some of the same blood in both of us", he said. "There is a look about your face that I seem to know. There are few so strong as the men of my blood."

"And whence is that blood?" asked the younger. "Who was your father?"

"He was Aidan, King of Alba."

"And he is still the king, and he is my father too. How did I fail to recognise you? You are my brother who overcame the Knight of the Riddles with his questions, and sent me home to look after our father's kingdom."

There was no more wrestling then, but embracing between the two brothers; a joyful return to the castle of the elder, with days of feasting to follow. Then the younger said he must return to their father's kingdom and tell him the tidings.

On he way he came to a great house, with a wide space in front of it, where twelve youths were playing shinty. He thought he would like a game, and they let him join them; but he did not play for long, for the weakest of them was stronger and better than he — he just could not keep up with them.

They all had a look of each other.

"Who was your father?" he asked.

"We do not know him", they told him. "We have never seen him. All we know is that we have the same father, but each of us has a different mother. And our mothers have told us that he is the brother of the lord of this land, The Knight of the White Shield."

"Then I am your father", he said. "And I remember well the twelve maidens who came to ask me the answer to the riddle my brother had set the old knight. Are they alive and well, your mothers?"

"They are indeed. And they will be wishing to meet you."

The prince went with them to meet the twelve mothers, from each of whom he had taken her plaid so many years ago. They welcomed him with laughter. There was no jealousy among them, only good friendship.

So there was more feasting, and at last the younger brother set off for his own kingdom. This time he was not alone, but accompanied by a company of twelve ladies and twelve youths — and to all of them his father, the old king, gave a kind welcome.

IRELAND

*Mermaids, seductive or gentle, come up out of the sea. There is an
awareness of countries beyond the sea — of France easily reached on
magic horses, even though these change to withered branches. There is
realism, and there is religion.*

The King of the Pipers and the Wonderful Tune

Maurice Connor was known as The King of the Pipers, for when he played he had everyone, young and old, merry or sad, dancing as if they had not a care in the world and nothing to do but dance. He knew every kind of tune, and so he was in great favour and demand all over the countryside.

His other title was Blind Maurice, for the poor fellow was without a glimmer of sight. His gift for music may have been bestowed on him in compensation, and he managed very well, thanks to his old mother who led him about on his journeys. If she was often weary, she did not complain, and she was as welcome as her son; people gave them both a warm welcome, they neither of them ever lacked food or shelter, and many a present was given to her: shoes for her feet, a cloak in winter.

One day on their travels she and Maurice came to Ballinskellig Bay in Iveragh: a rocky bit of the coast, rather cut off from the rest of the country. But there was a fine green field, and beyond it a shore of firm white sand, both places good for dancing. A dancing master had come to teach the people who were very willing to learn, but there was no music for them. The master had a small fiddle, but small skill in playing it, and anyhow he was fully occupied showing them the steps and calling out what they were to do.

So Maurice struck up a jig, and everyone began dancing better than they had ever danced before. Even the old people joined the younger ones. The dancing master was delighted, and asked for another dance tune. Maurice played it; and so it went on until people began to drop out, and sink down exhausted. Maurice himself was breathless.

"Will you have a dram?" asked the dancing-master. "I will, and thank you kindly."

"The trouble is I haven't such a thing as a glass. I've only this bottle of whisky."

"Och, that doesn't matter at all", said Maurice. "I can drink out of the bottle."

And so he did. He put the bottle to his mouth and drank

— not a dram, not a quarter or even half the bottle, but the whole bottle. The whisky flowed down his throat like a waterfall over a rock.

"That wasn't bad whisky at all", he told the dancing master genially, handing him the empty bottle. Then he put his mouth to his pipes and played again. If his playing before had been wonderful, it was nothing to the way he played now. None of them, not his old mother herself, had heard anything like it, and none of them knew the tune. How could they, for he was playing as it came to him through his own genius.

The people forgot that they were tired. Young and old they began dancing again, and danced as they had never danced before, as they never thought they could. The oldest of them danced as well as the youngest, the crippled as well as the nimblest. Maurice's old mother danced among the best. Maurice himself was dancing about even while he played. The whole green field was filled with a whirl of dancers. And the white beach below was filled too, for the crabs and lobsters came up out of the sea and danced on their claws, the fish swam up to the surface and leaped and whirled in the air — cod, whiting, haddock, and all — even the seals came swimming and rising in rhythm.

Then up from the sea came a lady, the loveliest any had ever seen, wafting along the shore like a wave. She had long green-gold hair and her dress was green and white, with flounces of seaweed. She had pearls in her hair and corals about her neck, and her teeth were white as pearls, her lips red as coral.

On she came over the beach, up to the field, and spoke to Maurice in a voice sweeter than any music he had ever heard. Though he could not see her beauty he was none the less allured by that voice.

She danced to him, following the wonderful tune.

"That is a sea tune", she told him, "you have drawn it from the waves. Maurice, King of the Pipers, you should be piper to a king: my father who is King-under-the-Sea will welcome you. And I would have you as my husband. All my father's treasure will be yours. Come with me, Maurice, come down to my father's palace and his kingdom beneath the waves."

All the time she spoke she was dancing, and Maurice was dancing too, and so were all the people and the fish and the crabs and lobsters and the seals, down on the beach and in the sea.

"Do not listen to her, Maurice my son", begged his old mother, coming close to him. "Do not be heeding her at all. She is only a fish and her father is king of the fishes. If you marry her, your children will be fishes and I'll never dare touch haddock or whiting, cod or crab as long as I live, for fear of eating my grandchildren".

But still the sea-princess spoke to him, luring him with her sweet voice, with the touch of her hand on his arm. She danced down towards the sea and he danced after her, still playing.

For a moment he turned to his mother.

"Mother I must follow her. I shall send you a piece of burnt wood every year, at this time, to show you I am still alive."

And what use that would be to her no one can say, but he was a man bewitched. As he danced towards the edge of the sea, following the princess, all the people drew back. The fish, the crabs, the seals, were all still. The princess danced into the sea and Maurice danced after her, still playing his pipes, down under the waves they went together, the seals and fish following. The beach was bare; the field was full of silent people. The old mother wept.

They were good to her, those people; they offered her a home, and she stayed with some of them for a little. But it was not for long; before the year was out she had died of a broken heart, and of starvation too, for never a bit of fish would she taste, for fear of eating one of her own grandchildren.

The sound of Maurice's pipes was heard from the depth of the sea. Next year, and the year after, on the same day a bit of burnt wood was found on the shore which was no good to anyone. It is said that you can still hear the sound of Maurice playing his wonderful tune. But if you go to listen, let me give you three bits of advice you'll do well to follow.

If you hear the tune, down there in the depth of the sea, don't try diving down to find him. If a mermaid comes up from the waves and speaks to you, bow politely and come away. Don't listen to her, don't answer her. If you were to bless yourself with the sign of the cross it would do no harm.

And don't try to swallow a bottle of whisky at one go, as if it were a glass of water. That will do you no good at all.

The Brown Bear of Norway

There was a king once in Ireland, in the days when Ireland had many kings in many small kingdoms, and he had three daughters: all very beautiful and loving and happy. There was little doubt that they would all find good husbands, probably royal. One day as they walked in the garden their father began teasing them, asking them who they would each choose to marry.

"The King of Ulster", said the eldest, "if that pleases you".

"It pleases me well", said her father "And I am thinking it will please the King of Ulster too. And whom would you choose, my dear?" he asked the second daughter.

"I would have the King of Munster, if it would please you".

"That too would please me well; and, I am thinking the King of Munster would agree. And how about you, my darling?" he asked his youngest daughter, who was his favourite, although he tried not to show it.

"There's no bridegroom I would choose but the

Brown Bear of Norway", was her startling reply.

"The Brown Bear of Norway! And who in the wide world is that?"

"It is one of old Nurse's tales I'm thinking", said the eldest girl. "She used always to be telling us tales of magic and enchantment".

"Yes; he'll be a prince under a spell", agreed the second girl, and the youngest did not contradict them.

Many a time she had heard from old Nurse of this hero, who was a man and a prince part of the time, and a brown bear the rest of the time. Her heart was full of pity for him and of hope that one day she might meet him and somehow set him free.

They came in from the garden, and the King told the Queen what their daughters had said. She was well pleased with the choice of the two elder daughters; indeed it may well be that the two kings had already spoken for the hand of those princesses. To her youngest she said indulgently:

"You think too much of those old tales of magic, my darling, but there is time enough yet. We'll have a fine young prince coming to ask for your hand, I've no doubt."

When the youngest princess, whose name was Rosaleen, went to bed that night, she thought again of the old tale.

"I wish I could see him, I wish I could help him, the poor Brown Bear of Norway", she said to herself before she fell asleep. She did not sleep long. It was still night when she awoke, not in her own room but in one far more splendid, though indeed hers was pretty and elegant enough. But this room was much larger; it was hung with tapestries, richly carpeted, and lit by golden lamps. By her bedside knelt a young and handsome prince.

"My dearest, kindest love", he said "You have come to save me. If you will marry me now you will, in time, set me free. You know I am under a spell. It was cast on me by an evil witch, whose daughter, no less evil, wanted to marry me. But I would not have her, and this is their revenge. By night I am myself, as you see me. This is my palace, in the heart of my kingdom. By day I am a brown bear, roaming the woods. But never have I hurt or harmed any one. Your wish, as you fell asleep, to see me and help me, has brought you here.

"If you will marry me, I may be set free from the enchantment after five years. You will need much patience and courage as well as love. We shall be together every night, but every morning I must leave you, and you will have to endure more than one sorrow and trial. But you are brave, my love, and I am sure of your help. When the five years are ended and I am free, we shall be happy all our lives together. Now, will you marry me?"

"I will; for I love you", the princess told him.

He left her then, and sent ladies to wait upon her and dress her in the finest silks and jewels she had ever seen, and lead her down to the hall where she was given a great welcome, everyone paying her homage. They were married at once, Rosaleen and the prince. There was a fine wedding feast, with music and dancing. It did not last long, however, for it was still night when the bride and bridegroom were led to their own room, where they fell asleep in each other's arms.

When Rosaleen awoke next morning the prince her husband had gone. There was a moment of tears, then, like the brave lass she was, she rose and bathed and dressed, her ladies waiting upon her, and went down to the hall.

The day passed quickly and pleasantly. All her life she had lived in a palace with gardens and orchards and park around it, but none of these could match the splendour, indoors and out-of-doors, in which she found herself now. Every room was full of treasures. There was a music room with every instrument she had heard of, and some she did not know. Rosaleen was musical, playing the harp and lute and singing very sweetly; so she promised herself many happy hours here. In another room were books of the old tales she loved. The garden was rich in flowers, the orchard in fruit, the park was wide, and there was a horse in the stables for her riding.

The day was full of delights to tell her husband when he came home at dusk. Then the darkness clouding the sky appeared to her much lovelier than the golden sunshine of the day.

They had supper, and sat talking, listening to music. Again they fell asleep in each other's arms. Again the princess woke to find herself alone. There was a moment of grief; but she put that away, and the second day was, like the first, full of pleasant things to tell the prince when he came home at that lovely time of darkness.

So a year passed, with much more happiness than sorrow, and at the end of it a baby prince was born. There was more than ever now to fill Rosaleen's day, more than ever to tell her husband at night.

It was summer, and darkness came late. One evening the prince and princess were sitting by an open window. She had the baby on her lap, and they both looked at him with love and joy. Suddenly a great eagle swooped down from the sky, flew in at the window, seized the baby by his clothes, and flew up and away, so swiftly that none could stop it, hardly even follow its flight.

That was a night of grief for the poor princess and the prince, with days of grief to follow. But she was brave, and she remembered what the prince had told her, that first night he came; that the five years would bring her many trials.

A year and a bit went by; the joy returned, with the birth of a little daughter. All went well at first; you may believe that the baby was never left alone, and never near an open window. The days were growing shorter, darkness came sooner, and one evening the prince had just come back. He was with the princess and their daughter in a room upstairs when they heard a commotion in the hall, the rush of feet, followed by loud cries. The door burst open and in ran a greyhound, swift as the wind. It snatched the baby from its mother's arms and ran out again, out of the palace, out of the garden and park, as swift almost as light so that none could follow. The second grief was even worse than the first, and it lasted a long time. Again Rosaleen was brave, again she had joy, when after a year and more a third baby, a second son was born. It was winter now, and the long nights were a comfort, her husband with her. One evening they sat by the fire, with the baby in her arms. The door and the window were fast shut. Everything was quiet, when suddenly a beautiful lady appeared — how she had come they could not tell — standing by the Princess. Very gently but irresistibly she took the baby from his mother's arms — and disappeared.

This was the worst sorrow of all. The poor princess fell ill and the prince grieved deeply for her. As she became a little better she begged him pathetically:

"Will you let me go back, only for a short time, to my mother and father and sisters?" He was reluctant to let her go, but he could not refuse her sad, gently pleading.

"Go, then, my darling, and God keep you. You have only to wish, before you go to sleep, that you will waken in your father's palace. When you want to come back, then wish to be here with me. But please, I implore you, do not stay long away from me."

"I will not indeed; only a few days."

That night they took a very loving farewell (but only for a little time) of each other. Rosaleen murmured her wish, and fell asleep. She awoke in her own bed in her own room in her father's palace.

It was all just as she had left it. She rang the silver bell which stood by the bed and her old nurse rushed in, bewildered, overwhelmed, laughing and sobbing at once. The nurse went to tell the queen, and Rosaleen's two sisters, who had come on a visit, each with her husband and children; for not long after Rosaleen's disappearance they had married, one the King of Ulster, the other the King of Munster, just as they had wished. Now they came running with the queen their mother for a joyful reunion. Then Rosaleen was led to her father, who wept for joy as he embraced her; she met her brothers-in-law and the children, for her sisters each had three lovely children, just as Rosaleen had had; as she kissed them she thought of her own lost ones and her heart was sore, and tears sprang into her eyes. Yet it was a comfort to be home again with her own folk, and the day passed happily. Her mother and sisters were eager to know what had happened to her. They questioned her gently, and gradually she told them the whole story; of her happiness, and her sorrow at the spell which still marred her life with her husband. It had been good to return home, but she must not stay long, for her place was with her husband.

"Indeed you must go back to him", said her mother. "But we must do something to help you."

"I have an idea", said the old nurse. "The new hen-wife who has come is a wise woman. Let the princess consult her; she may have help and good counsel to offer."

The queen and the sisters agreed, and persuaded Rosaleen to go to the hen-wife, who told her:

"What you must do is to find and burn the bearskin. Then your husband will be set free."

"But how am I to find it? I never see him go, I never see him come back. He just suddenly appears with me again, as night falls."

"Do you sleep heavily? Does he give you anything to drink at night?" The princess remembered: "Yes, he always brings me a cup of sweet, delicious wine."

"Then do not drink it."

After a day or two Rosaleen longed so much to return to her husband that she bade farewell, not without sadness, to her mother and father and sisters. That night she murmured her wish to be with her husband again, and next morning she awoke in their room in their own palace. He was not there — she was prepared for that; but her ladies and everyone in the palace welcomed her joyfully, and the day passed quickly; at nightfall her husband came to her, and their joy was great.

That night he brought, as usual, her cup of wine, but she was able to put it aside without tasting it and without his noticing. That night she slept lightly and awoke early to find him still asleep beside her. She lay very still and quiet, and presently he awoke, went over to a panel in the wall, slid it open and took out a brown bearskin. This he put on, and dropping on four paws padded quietly out of the room. The day passed; at nightfall he came to her in his true form. When he brought her cup of wine she contrived not only to put it aside, but to change it with his cup of undrugged wine. They had so much to talk about that he did not notice. He fell asleep almost at once, and slept profoundly. The princess hardly slept at all; before the first glimmer of dawn she rose, walked silently to the panel in the wall, opened it and took out the bearskin. This she carried down to the hall where the fire still glowed. She laid more peats upon it, stirred it to flame, laid the bearskin on top and saw it burn to ashes. Then slowly and fearfully she returned to their room to find her husband standing at the open panel and the empty cupboard.

He turned to look at her, with a face of anguish and reproach.

"Most unhappy woman, what have you done to me and to yourself? The worst was over. One more year would have brought the end of the enchantment, and my release. Could you not have waited? Who told you of this, who bade you destroy the bearskin?"

"The hen-wife at my father's palace", Rosaleen confessed weeping.

"The witch herself. She knew the end of her power was near. Now I must go a long way from here. We may never meet again."

He kissed her sorrowfully and went out. The princess hurriedly threw on some clothes, a cloak, put strong shoes on her feet and ran after him. He was already at the edge of the park. She followed swiftly, keeping him in sight. He came to the foot of a hill, and she followed; when she reached the place he was at the top of the hill, when she had climbed there he was down in the valley, and another hill lay beyond. All day long she followed him, never losing sight but never catching up with him; up and down hills, across field and valley, until at dusk he turned off into a lane. As she followed he went into a cottage. The princess knocked and was admitted. Inside the cottage it was warm and welcoming. A kind-looking woman was there, and the prince sat by the fire with her own little son on his knee.

He spoke gently to the princess, telling her that the woman was his sister who, in form of an eagle, had carried away their son. "It was for his own protection from the witch. He has been well guarded ever since, and is safe here."

The woman of the house looked after them well, washing their tired feet and rubbing them with a soothing ointment. The little boy knew his mother after a time, and went to her arms. They had supper together, and the boy was put to bed.

"We are together tonight", the prince told his wife. "But tomorrow I must leave you; not as a bear, for I shall keep my own true form, but my memory of you will gradually become clouded, and I shall not know you."

In the morning she rose in time to see him go. Before she left the kind sister gave her a magic gift; a pair of scissors.

"Whatever you cut with these scissors, the coarsest stuff, or even paper, will be turned to silk. Now a blessing on your journey, and I shall cherish your son."

Walking swiftly and running, Rosaleen kept her husband in sight, up hill, down in the valley, on and on until dusk, when again he turned off into a lane, and entered a cottage. The princess followed and found him sitting by the fire with their little daughter on his knee, and with them a woman, comely and with a kindly expression.

"This is my second sister", the prince told her. "It was she who came as a greyhound and carried off our daughter to safety."

The little girl came to her mother; the two women embraced and spoke courteously and lovingly to each other. The kind sister bathed their feet, and gave them supper. The night brought rest. In the morning the prince left, with neither a look nor a word for his wife, but she was prepared for that and ready to follow him. Before she left the good sister gave her a magic gift: a comb.

"Whenever you comb your hair, gold and jewels will fall from it. Now God go with you and bring you safely back. I shall look after your child."

This day's journey was not very different from the two previous days' journey. At dusk the prince had come to a cottage which he entered, the princess following. By the fire sat a gentle and lovely women holding a baby, the tiny son of the prince and princess. Rosaleen recognised her as the beautiful lady who had come so swiftly and mysteriously and carried off the baby.

Again they were happy and peaceful together. The princess held her baby, the kind sister cared for them, the night brought sleep. Again, early in the morning the prince went away, not looking at his wife, not bidding her farewell. She followed, but first that kind sister gave her a magic gift.

"Take this spindle, my dear. It will spin a golden thread. May it bring you golden happiness."

The prince was walking far ahead, the princess ran and walked after him keeping him in sight, until they came to the edge of a wood. The trees opened to let the prince through, but when the princess came up they closed like a dark wall. Then she thought of a way.

"By my three magic gifts I command you to let me pass",

she called and the trees drew apart. She walked into the wood, along a green path, to the further edge. There stood not far away a grim castle with a high wall. The gate opened to let the prince enter, but closed again in the face of the princess, and here she dared not try the power of her gifts.

Beside the wood was a cottage, that of the woodman and his wife. Rosaleen knocked at the door, and humbly and gently begged for shelter.

"Let me work for you", she pleaded, "I ask no wages, only shelter."

They were kind people and they took her in. When they had finished supper she was shown to a room with a bed and table and chair. She thanked the good woman most courteously.

"A great lady, that", said the woman to her husband. "In some trouble too. The mistress up at the castle had a hand in it, I've no doubt."

"Like enough", agreed the husband.

Next day the housewife talked to her guest. The castle was that of a witch and her daughter. Years ago there had been a prince living there, not by his own will. He had escaped; but now it seemed he had come back. He was sad and silent, he walked about the castle and the park, but did not come beyond the gate. The princess listened. A day or two passed. One day she found her hostess beginning to cut out a dress from some coarse linen.

"Let me do that", said Rosaleen, and carried the stuff to her room where she began cutting it with her own magic scissors. As she cut, the stuff changed into the most beautiful rich silk. Quickly she took her spindle, and began spinning a golden thread, with which she sewed the dress. Then she combed her hair and drew out a gold brooch to fasten the new gown, and took it to the woman of the house, who was overwhelmed with pleasure and gratitude.

The woman went up most days to help in the castle, and of course she talked about this. One day, a day of glorious sunshine, the prince was tempted to walk beyond the castle grounds, and he found the princess sitting outside the cottage. He looked at her, puzzled and sad. She was so lovely, so gentle — and there was something more. It almost seemed as if he had once seen her in a dream, which he could barely remember. He walked back to the castle.

Meanwhile the gossip about the fine silk gown had come to the ears of the witch's daughter. Full of curiosity and greed, she walked down to the cottage. The princess had gone into her room, and was standing by the table, at the open window, cutting a dress out of paper, which, as the magic scissors touched it, turned to fine silk.

"What will you take for these scissors?", asked the witch-daughter greedily, staring in.

"One thing only; to be allowed to spend the night in the prince's bedroom."

The witch-daughter was about to say rudely: "Not likely, you impudent hussy", when she thought a nasty deceitful thought, and replied:

"All right. Come up tonight and bring the scissors."

The princess came and was met by the witch-daughter, who led her to the prince's room and demanded the scissors. Then she withdrew, laughing maliciously. Rosaleen approached the bed where her husband lay asleep. She kissed him, she spoke to him and shook him gently, but he did not waken, nor even stir. Then she sang to him:

Four long years I was married to thee,
Three sweet babes I bore to thee,
Brown Bear of Norway
Won't you turn to me?

But he did not stir or turn. Sadly the princess went back to the cottage in the morning. Once again the prince came wandering past the cottage, looking sadder and more lost than ever; but he did not know her.

Not long afterwards the witch's daughter came again. The princess sat by an open window combing her hair; and as she combed, pearls and diamonds fell on her lap.

"What will you take for that comb?" asked the witch-girl.

"The same price as before: leave to spend the night in the prince's bedroom."

The witch-girl agreed at once, thinking this girl was a poor fool. That night Rosaleen again came to the castle, and was taken to her husband's room, where she gave the comb to the witch-daughter. The prince was asleep, and he did not stir.

Again she sang her sad little song; she thought he moved slightly, with a little frown on his forehead, as if about to awake; but again he lapsed into immobility, and not a flicker of life did he show.

He came past the cottage in the morning, and this time he stopped to wish her good-day.

"Do you sleep well, sir?" she asked.

"Once I did not; for many nights I lay wakeful and troubled. But last night and the night before I have slept deeply indeed. Only last night I had a shadowy dream which I cannot remember." "Do you have a drink at night?" "I do; a cup of wine." "Sir, I beg you, do not drink tonight."

He looked at her, puzzled; but he promised to do as she asked.

He went away, the princess sat by her open window with her spindle, spinning a long gold thread. The witch-daughter came and looked in.

"What will you take for that spindle?"

"The same as I asked for the scissors and the comb."

The witch-daughter nearly laughed aloud in mockery.

"Agreed", she said. "Come to the castle tonight."

The princess came, was taken to the room, and handed over her spindle. The prince lay with his eyes closed, but was not asleep. He opened his eyes and looked at Rosaleen, a little puzzled. She sang her song:

Four long years I was married to thee,
Three sweet babes I bore to thee;
Brown Bear of Norway won't you turn to me?"

Up he leapt, and they wasted no time over explanations. At once they ran hand in hand from the room, down to the hall, out into the courtyard and away. The servants who saw them followed; word came to others, and the whole household, all but the witch-girl and her mother, came streaming out. As they came the walls of the castle began to rumble, and there was a dull rumbling sound which gradually became a roar. Hardly had they all reached the park when the castle came crashing to the ground in ruins, over the heads of the two evil witches.

The prince and princess ran to the woodman's cottage, where they spent the rest of the night. Early in the morning they departed, thanking those good people for their kindness, and promising to send for them and take them into their own service. That day, travelling quickly and happily, they came to the cottage where the prince's sister was taking care of their baby. That was a joyful meeting. Next day they went on to the second sister, and their little daughter; on the third day to the sister who had care of their elder son. They all travelled together now, home to the prince's palace, for a welcome such as has rarely been known.

A messanger was dispatched to bring the good wood-keeper and his wife, who gladly accepted work in the royal household. After a few days the prince, princess, and their three children made a swift journey to the palace of Rosaleen's mother and father. Their joy was beyond words, for they had lived in grief since her second departure; the wicked henwife had long since disappeared, and they had feared witchcraft.

The King and Queen of Ulster, the King and Queen of Munster, were summoned to the palace. For many days or even weeks of feasting and rejoicing they were all together, and then the three families went to their own homes. The great feasting was over, but the happiness lasted until their lives' end. And always when the children begged for a story from their mother or nurse or grandmother, they were not satisfied until they heard yet again the tale of The Brown Bear of Norway.

Guleesh

Guleesh was a quiet, decent lad, rather keeping himself to himself when he was not working on his farm. He had a great memory for old tales and legends told by the fire, on winter nights, some of them told him by his old grandmother. Near his house stood a rath, or fairy-mound, and one evening as it was growing dark he stood there by himself; not perhaps the wisest thing to do, for you never know what the wee folk may be after. He was about to go into the house when he heard a great noise of voices and the rushing of feet. The voices grew louder, and it was clear that they came from inside the rath.

"My horse and saddle and bridle!" "My horse and saddle and bridle!" called one voice after another, and for the fun of it Guleesh called out too:

"My horse and saddle and bridle!"

The door of the rath opened, and out came a procession of little men each on a tiny horse; at the end of this cavalcade came a larger horse, without a rider — it looked big and strong enough to carry Guleesh, and it was ready saddled and bridled, in fine green leather.

"You're welcome, Guleesh", said the leader of the troop, a little old man with a long beard. "You can ride with us over

the sea to France and help us to carry off the King's daughter.
Your horse will easily take the pair of you; and you're a fine
strong lad, so you can easily carry the princess out of the palace
when I give you the word."

Well Guleesh was a great lover of adventure, so he
mounted his horse and rode off with the rest to the sea-coast.

There the leader called: "Hie over cap! Hie over cap!" And
at once his horse rose into the air and flew high over the sea.
The others said the same words and followed, and so did
Guleesh, and they all landed safely on the shore.

"You're in France now, Guleesh, my fine lad", the leader
said. "And listen to what I'll be telling you about what you are
to do. We'll ride to the king's palace, and I'll put a spell on you
and the rest of us, so that we'll be invisible, but shall be able to
see everyone. The king and queen are marrying their daughter
tonight to a man she has little liking for; and we have a great
liking for her. She will be the first princess we've carried off, so
listen carefully to what is to happen. When the right moment
comes I'll put the spell on her, and she will be invisible to
everyone but ourselves. You will carry her out in your arms,
and will put her on your horse, and mount yourself; then we'll
all ride off to the sea coast again."

Guleesh was not sure if he liked the look of the little man;
but he was in the adventure now, whether he liked it or not. So
they rode off again swiftly till they came to the palace of the
king. It was lit up with a thousand brilliant lights, and the
sound of music and dancing filled the whole palace. The
courtyard was quiet and empty. The little old man dismounted, they all followed, and tethered their horses. Then
the leader spoke some strange words and led the way to the
door of the palace.

It opened at another word, and they all trooped in. No
one took any notice, for no one could see them. The hall was
full of light and splendour. The king and queen sat on their
thrones, clad in velvet and magnificent robes, and crowned
with gold and jewels. Beside the king sat the bridegroom also
arrayed in splendid clothes, but Guleesh did not much like the
look of him. Beside the queen sat the princess, all in white. Her
face was lovely, but it was the saddest face Guleesh had ever
seen, for there were tears in her eyes; and this was not how a

bride ought to look. The king and queen were a handsome couple, but their features lacked the light of love and kindliness.

Guleesh soon decided that there would be no harm at all in helping to carry off the princess. Presently the music stopped and the dancers were still. There was a bishop there in his robes and mitre, and he moved towards an altar at the end of the hall. The king and queen rose and followed him, with the bridegroom and the poor bride, but just at that moment the little man must have pronounced his spell.

Everyone looked, shuddered, and gasped. They could see no princess! But Guleesh could see her, and so could the wee folk, rather shadowy indeed, but she was there all the same, and at a word in his ear from the little man he went to her, lifted her in his arms, and followed his companions out of the hall, into the courtyard. The horses were there, Guleesh lifted the princess to the saddle, mounted himself, and as the little man spoke the word of command they all rode off swiftly towards the sea-coast. The people who came pouring out of the palace could see none of them.

"Hie over cap! Hie over cap!" they all called out when they reached the sea. Again their horses rose high into the air, and flew over the waves. They landed safely and rode on to the rath where they dismounted.

"You've done well, Guleesh", said the leader. "And there will be some gold for you. So now set the princess down, and I'll lead her within; and goodnight to you."

Guleesh liked less than ever the look of the little old man. He lifted the princess gently from the saddle, set her on her feet, and said to her: "I mark you for myself, and I bless you with the sign of the cross, in the Name of God."

The leader shrieked with fury.

"You'll pay for this, Guleesh, you who think yourself so clever!" He pointed his finger at the princess and muttered some words. "She is dumb now, and never a word will you hear from her."

He spoke another spell. The door of the rath opened, the whole company disappeared inside, and the door closed behind them. Where the horses had stood there were now only some withered branches of trees, Guleesh's was the beam of a plough sticking out of a pile of rubbish.

Guleesh held the princess by the hand and spoke gently to her. She looked at him, startled perhaps yet not terrified; Guleesh spoke again, telling her he would protect her. She looked at him gently, with a little smile, then touched her mouth to show that she was dumb.

"The best thing to do", Guleesh went on, "will be to take you to the priest. He is a good man and is sure to have a plan."

She gave him her hand, and they walked together to the priest's house. That good man was well used to being wakened in the middle of the night and called to help some one in sickness or at the point of death, but never had he received such a strange guest or heard such a strange tale. He was a wise old man, and knew something besides his Latin and his theology. First he gave the princess his blessing, and signed her with the cross, which brought a look of peace to her face. Then, having heard Guleesh's tale he said: "Haven't I told you often enought not to spend so much time by the rath? Now what are we to do? The princess had better stay here; my housekeeper will look after her, and I'll let people think that she is my niece, who is afflicted with dumbness, and has come to stay with me for a bit. Then I'll write some letters. There are often merchants coming this way who go on over the sea to other lands, and they can carry letters to the King of France. Now I'll call my housekeeper, who will give this poor lass some breakfast and put her to bed. And you go home to your own breakfast, Guleesh, you foolish fellow, and have a bit of sleep if you can, and go about your work. There will be a bite of supper here for you, if you come back in the evening."

This Guleesh very willingly did. The princess soon settled down, and the kind housekeeper looked after her well; she smiled and nodded, or smiled and shook her head when they spoke to her; and as time went on she and Guleesh and the priest became better and better at sign language, and came to understand each other very well. Guleesh knew now that he had fallen in love with her when he saw her in her father's palace, and he fell deeper and deeper in love every day.

There was a bit of talk at first in the parish, but it was accepted that this was the priest's poor afflicted niece, and she was indeed a gentle lass with a sweet smile for everyone. The housekeeper was a discreet woman, not given either to asking or answering many questions. No word at all came from France. The priest thought his letters must have been lost, and Guleesh certainly hoped they had.

A year went past, and one evening Guleesh was again sitting outside, beyond his own wall, near the rath. The moon came up, and shone through a cloud of mist; the stars were brilliant in the sky. It was very still, with only the sound of the flight of wild geese overhead. Gradually he became aware of a sound like a rising wind, or like waves rolling and dashing on the shore, or even the sound of a great waterfall. There was a great wind blowing in the trees, and there were strange sounds coming from inside the rath. Guleesh crouched down and listened, and heard exactly what he had heard a year ago — for he remembered that it was this November night a year earlier that he had heard the voices calling:

"My horse and saddle and bridle! My horse and saddle and bridle!" Out they came, the whole troop of them riding their horses. Guleesh — and he was the bold one to do it — cried out too:

"My horse and saddle and bridle!" But never a horse appeared for him. Two of the riders at the tail of the cavalcade looked at him, and laughed.

"Isn't he the bold one, thinking he can come with us again?" said one, "He tricked us that time, but he won't trick us again", said the other. "Och yes, he is bold enough, but isn't he a fool not to know there's a plant growing at his own door that will put her speech back into the princess? Maybe we should be telling him."

"Och never mind; leave him alone."

So they rode off swiftly after the others, and Guleesh rose to his feet and stood staring and wondering.

"Is this mischief they're up to, and will this plant be poison? Or have they some good will to me, after all?"

He went up to his door, and there looked at the strange plant which had always grown there, but which he had never dared to pluck. He went to bed for an hour or two, but he could not sleep for thinking. At dawn he got up, went out and cut the plant. It had seven little branches, and on each branch seven leaves that appeared to be filled with a white sap.

Guleesh carried it into the house, He cut off the leaves and cut the stalk; a thick, oily white juice came out. He collected it in a little pot, added some water and put it on the fire to come to the boil and simmer. Then he poured it into a cup. Should he taste it? Or would it be poison? Was this a vengeance by the wee folk in the rath?

Well there was at least a chance that the fairy man had spoken the truth and meant him no ill. Guleesh made the sign of the cross over the cup, dipped his finger into the liquid, and tasted it. It was sweet and thick, and he took another sip and then another. Then he went to bed and slept deeply all that day. It was night when he awoke, so he had another sip, and went to sleep again until morning when he awoke feeling fine and fresh, clear in the head, and full of hope.

Carrying the cup carefully he walked to the priest's house, and found the good man and the princess at breakfast. They wondered at seeing him so early, but gave him a kind welcome.

"What is this you are carrying, Guleesh?" asked the priest. Guleesh told them the whole story. "And I've tasted it myself, and I've never felt better in my life."

He presented it to the princess, who tasted it cautiously. She took another sip, and immediately fell asleep, though she had not been awake for long. All that day and all the following night she slept, and woke in the morning. Guleesh was waiting for the result impatiently, while the priest was in great anxiety.

"Did you sleep well, my dear?"

"I never slept better", she said, smiling and laughing.

There was great thanksgiving then, from the priest and from Guleesh, and she could join them in their words.

Then she looked drowsy again, and so did Guleesh, for it was a powerful juice.

"Go home again, Guleesh", the priest told him, and come back in the evening." Guleesh very happily did as he was told. He too fell asleep, but when he awoke he was alert and lively. He found the princess and the priest waiting for him. The priest had told her something of what had happened, of how Guleesh had saved her, and what a good fellow he was.

Guleesh fell on his knees before her and told her of his

love. There was no sadness on her face as she listened, nor were there any tears in her eyes.

"Will you marry me, princess, though I'm a poor man?"

"I will, for you saved me, and I have learnt to love you dearly."

What better answer could there be, or what better end to the story? The priest married them, and Guleesh took her home. There was not a wife in the place to surpass her in gentleness and love, and no man could come near Guleesh in the love he felt then, and always, for his bride. They lived there until the end of their lives, and they both lived to a ripe old age, nor was there ever a shadow of grief over their happiness.

Changelings

It is a dreadful thing for a mother to find her own child taken away, and an ugly changeling left in its place. The Other People sometimes play this cruel trick, for they like to have a human baby. This is what happened to one poor woman, called Mary. She went to help the reapers in the field, leaving her baby wrapped up in her shawl — safe as she thought, in a corner where no one was likely to come, and besides, the reapers were all at work within sight. But when she came to take him home, it was an ugly, wrinkled little creature she found, and not her own fine baby boy. She knew at once that he had been put there, so off she went to consult a wise women.

"You must harden your heart, Mary my dear", said the wise woman, "and treat the creature ill. Give it little or nothing to eat or drink. Take the blanket off it in the cradle, and let it lie cold. It will do no harm at all if you give it a severe pinch or nip from time to time."

Mary went home. She was a kind woman, and would never have been hard on any human child, no matter how serious the offence. But she would do anything to get rid of this dreadful creature. So hardly a bite or a sup did she give it, that day or the next; she took the blanket off the cradle, though it was bitterly cold; she even gave it a nip and a pinch from time to time.

The creature did not like this treatment at all. With a yell and a screech he flew up out of the cradle, across to the open door, out and away. And there in his place lay the real baby asleep. And you may be very sure he had no nips or pinches from his mother, only some milk and some honey and a soft blanket over him, her arms about him, her voice singing a lullaby.

Another woman called Kate had rather more trouble. When she found an ugly changeling in the cradle one day, she went straight to the wise woman and was told what to do.

"Put the big pot on the fire to boil. Then break a dozen eggs. Do what you like with them, but put all the empty shells into the pot and let them come to the boil, and simmer away."

Kate went back to her house, collected the eggs, broke

them, and put all the shells into the pot she had set on the fire.
The water came to the boil, and she watched it carefully to see
the egg shells all bobbing about.

The creature in the cradle, over in the corner, sat up and
asked, in an ugly croak:

"What are you doing, hanging over the pot on the fire like
that?"

"You be quiet. I'm making a brew of egg shells. Lie down
and go to sleep."

"I've lived a thousand years and more, but never have I
seen anyone cooking empty eggshells till now."

Kate knew then, for certain, what sort of a thing this was.
She picked up the poker and ran towards the cradle to hit him,
but in her haste she tripped and fell, and the poker flew out of
her hand. She was up again at once, picked up the poker, and
ran to the cradle. The door was open, the changeling was
gone; in the cradle lay her own darling child.

I think that Kate gave the wise woman something better
to drink than a brew of egg shells!

The Sunken Palace: King Corc and Fior Usga

Where there is now a deep lough in County Cork there once stood a palace, that of King Corc. It was a beautiful palace and was surrounded by a fine garden and park. The king had many treasures, but what he valued most was the well in his courtyard. The water was pure and clear as crystal, sparkling like diamonds. It would quench any thirst; washing in it would leave your face clear and fresh; it would cleanse and heal wounds. Naturally the people came every day to draw from the well, and fill a jug or a pail. The king was right to value it, but it was not right to grudge it as he did. He had a high wall built round it, with a locked door. The princess (his only daughter) kept the key, and anyone who wanted a cupful or a jugful had to come and beg it from her. The name given her was Fior Usga, which means Fair Water.

One evening there was a grand ball at the palace. Among the guests was a young man whom no one knew, but whom everyone admired, including the king and his daughter. They were sure he must be a prince, for he was so handsome, so courteous, so richly dressed, and he danced so well. He danced with many of the ladies, much to their pleasure, but most of all with the princess.

When supper was served he sat by her. It was a delicious feast of food and wine, fruit and sweetmeats. The young man ate and drank well:

"But there is one thing lacking, sir", he said to the king. "The dancing and the rich food have given me a thirst which no wine can quench; only a glass of pure water can do that."

"That you will have", said the king. "My daughter, whose name is Fior Usga (Fair Water), will take you to the well. The water there is such as you have rarely tasted. It will surely quench your thirst."

He gave the young man a great golden cup. The princess took the key and led him to the well in the courtyard, and opened the door in the wall that guarded the well.

They looked down. The water was deep and clear, sparkling like crystal or diamonds. The princess took the cup,

bent down to fill it, and the weight of it drew her into the well,
deep, deep down; and the young man went away. The water
began to rise. It flooded the well, brimmed over the edge,
filled the courtyard, rushing up and bubbling over as if glad to
be free from imprisonment.

The water swept into the hall of the palace, into every
room, overwhelming the king and all his company. Yet no
one cried out in terror.

The water swept on, submerging the palace, filling garden and park, then the whole valley beyond. Now there was a
great lough, and away down in its depths the palace could be
seen, exactly as it had been when it had rested on dry land. The
people appeared to be moving about, the king and the princess
among them.

Some folk say that the palace can still be seen, deep down
beneath the waves in the lough near Kinsale. Sometimes the
people in it can be seen too, moving about and dancing, the
king and his daughter among them.

Many have thought that this was a punishment for the
king's meanness and greed in grudging the fair water to his
people. It may be that in time he will have expiated his fault,
and that the waters will sink, the palace rise again on dry land.
When that day comes, the well in the courtyard will surely be
open to all who come to draw water from its clear spring.

The Bride from the Sea: The Mermaid's Cap

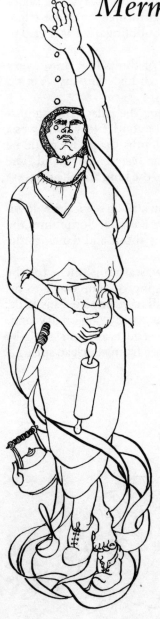

A young fisherman, Dick Fitzgerald, was standing on the shore one fine morning, smoking his pipe. It was early, there was no one else about, no one to talk to, and he felt a bit lonely. Then he saw on a rock a lovely girl; she sat combing her long green-gold hair. She was dressed in sea-green, and beside her lay a little sea-green cap.

Dick had heard from his grandmother, who knew many an old tale, that when a mermaid (or merrow, as some people call them) comes ashore she wears a little cap; she may take it off to comb her hair, but she must put it on again before she slips back into the sea and descends under the waves.

Dick walked quietly across. In a moment, while her head was turned, he had picked up the mermaid's cap and put it in his pocket. With tears in her eyes she begged him:

"Give me back my cap and I shall dive down to my father's palace and bring you up treasures of gold and coral and pearls." But Dick shook his head.

"Give me my cap, take my hand, and come down with me to my father's kingdom. He will welcome you and you shall be my husband, and king of under-the-waves."

But he still refused.

"It is better to stay on land", he said. "Come with me to my own house; it is a poor place indeed, but there will be a home for you always".

She looked at him sadly. She did not consent, but she did not refuse. Then Dick thought that indeed it was a poor little house he was taking her to. Her bed would be of straw.

"There will be many fine beds in your father' palace, I'm thinking?"

"Oh yes; we have fourteen oyster beds", the mermaid told him.

Dick was too polite to smile, but he felt reassured. He took the girl by the hand — it was soft and white, with long fingers, and between the fingers a fine web — and led her away. Before they went, she looked out over the sea, whispered a farewell to her father and mother, bidding them not to keep breakfast for her.

Dick took her to his cottage, and went to tell the priest and ask him to marry them. The priest was reluctant.

"She is not human. She is only a fish and your children may be fish." But Dick persuaded him, and he agreed to marry the fisherman and the mermaid.

This bride from the sea made a very good wife to Dick, and a good and tender mother to the three children who were born to them — a girl, followed by two boys: they were not in the least fishlike, but very bonny and good. She seemed to bring her husband luck, too. He was a sober, hard-working fellow, and everything went well with them.

People liked her too, for her gentle ways, and her good house-wifery. Very often she was begged to come and sing a child to sleep, for she had a lovely voice, and this she was always willing to do.

So time passed happily. One day Dick found he had to go to Tralee, the town near their village. It was a fine bright day, the two elder children were playing outside, the baby lying asleep in his cradle.

"I'll be giving the place a good clean", the mermaid wife

said to herself. When she had finished she looked up at the **rafters**. What was that dusty old thing half hanging over? An old net? It would be better of a good washing, and she would spread it out in the sun to dry.

She reached up with a stick, caught the net and drew it down. And with it came the green cap which Dick had hidden there, on the night after he had brought her home.

Over the years she had thought at times of the kingdom beneath the waves, of her own father and mother; thought a little sadly and with a little longing, but not too clearly or sadly, for her husband and children filled her heart.

Now memories came rushing in like the tide. With them came a great longing to see her own people again.

She walked over to the cradle, looked tenderly at her sleeping baby; walked to the open door and watched her children so happily at play together. She thought of Dick, her good husband. They had been happy together, with never a quarrel, never a harsh word from him, and never had he looked at another woman.

But the memories were sweeping in, stronger than before, like huge powerful waves. There seemed to be a faint sound of music far off.

Again she went to the cradle, kissed her baby very gently so as not to waken him. From the door she called to her other two children who came running to her. She kissed them lovingly, bade the little girl be kind to her brothers, and to her father.

Then she put the green cap on her head and walked swiftly away, down to the shore, down to the edge of the sea. The waves were lapping around her feet. Now she could hear clearly the sound of music coming up from the depths.

She climbed on to the rock and dived down, into the green waters. The music sounded clear and loud, and then was silent.

When Dick came home he found his children crying. The little daughter told how their mother had walked away, with a green cap on her head; gone so swiftly that they could not follow. The net lay on the floor. Dick knew what had happened. Why had he not destroyed the cap altogether?

The sea-woman never came back to her husband and

children. Did she forget — or did she remember sometimes, with sadness? Dick never forgot. Until the end of his life he remembered her; he never married again, or gave any other woman a thought.

WALES

No fairy mounds here, or changelings, and all that is seen of a malignant being is the hand which has seized Rhiannon's baby, and which steals the foal; we are not told what happens to the owner of the hand. Rome lies in the background in one tale, and the Emperor comes over the sea. Two brothers are kings, one in England, and one in France. History and geography are bewitched almost out of knowledge.

Lludd and Llefelys

Beli the Great, King of Britain, was succeeded by his eldest son Lludd, who ruled wisely and well. He rebuilt the walls of his city Caer Ludd, and had the citizens build good houses for themselves. The name of that city changed gradually: from Caer Lludd to Caer Lundein, then Lundein, and, long after his death, to London.

Lludd had three younger brothers, of whom his favourite was the youngest Llefelys, for whom he had a profound respect as well as great affection: he was a particularly wise young man. They were constant companions until Llefelys became King of France, which came about in this way. The late King of France had left no son, only a daughter who became queen, and for whom a good marriage was therefore very important.

"Here, surely, is your bride", Lludd said to his young brother. "Let us sail for France."

They sailed over the sea, and in France they were courteously received and welcomed. The nobles met in council to decide whom their young queen should

marry. Llefelys was regarded with favour, the queen and he
fell happily in love with each other, and the marriage and
coronation were duly celebrated. So Lludd returned to Britain
well pleased.

But before long troubles darkened the land: three disas-
ters came upon the people, which none could avert or overcome. The first was an invasion by a strange folk called the
Coranieid. They had a sense of hearing so acute that whatever
folk said to each other, even in a whisper, could be carried by
the wind to their ears; it was thus impossible to make any plot
against them, without their knowing it.

The second plague came on May Eve. It was a frightful
scream heard all over the island, piercing every ear, bringing
panic and terror to everyone. Strong men became as weak as
water, women miscarried, young people fainted in terror. The
cows gave no milk, no animal could bring forth its young; the
grass and trees withered. Yet none could see or discover where
that dreadful scream came from.

The third trouble fell upon Lludd alone and his household. No meat or drink could be stored in his castle, for it
disappeared; only what was eaten and drunk at one meal was
safe. And no thief could be detected.

Lludd did a wise thing. The wisest man he knew was his
brother Llefelys, so he set sail for France to meet and consult
him. Llefelys came to meet him, the two fleets were in sight of
each other, the two kings met by themselves on one ship.
Lludd told his brother about the three plagues. Before they
spoke further Llefelys produced a horn through which they
could talk utterly unheard by anyone, their words guarded
from any breath of wind that might carry them to the Coranieid. Then Llefelys gave his counsel:

"I am giving you a bag of insects. Take care of them, keep
a few in case you need them later, but the rest you are to steep
in a great quantity of water. Then summon all the people, your
own folk and the Coranieid to an assembly, saying that you
will make peace between them when they are all gathered.
Then sprinkle them with the water. Your own people will take
no harm at all from this, but the Coranieid will be extermin-
ated.

"As for the second plague. That frightful scream comes

from the fighting of two dragons, one who lives hidden in Britain, and the other from a foreign land. On May Eve they meet and fight, first on the ground, then flying up into the air. From their conflict comes that disastrous scream.

"It will soon be May Eve. Before it comes, have an exact measurement made of the island, from north to south, from east to west. In the centre have a pit dug. Then have a tub filled with the strongest mead that can be brewed, and lower it into the pit. Cover the mouth of the pit with a silken cloth, and keep watch. You will see the two dragons meet on the ground; they will fly up into the air and fight until both are exhausted; then both will fall upon the sheet which covers the pit. Their weight will drag it down, and they will sink into the tub of mead and drink until they are in a deep slumber.

"Climb down then and wrap the sheet about them. Have them carried away to the strongest place in the island, where you must have a stone coffin ready for them. Bury them deep beneath earth and rocks, and they will trouble you no more.

"Now for the third plague. The thief who steals your food and wine is a magician. He comes in the dark when folk are asleep, and any who may be awake are lulled by the sweet music he plays. You must keep watch one night, alone and armed. Have close by you a huge tub of ice-cold water. Whenever you feel sleep come upon you, plunge quickly into the tub, and be ready for an immediate encounter."

Lludd thanked his brother with all his heart. His admiration and gratitude were profound, and they parted with mutual blessing.

As soon as he came home Lludd steeped half the insects in water, keeping the other half in case of future need. He summoned an assembly of all the people, his own and the Coranieid, and when they were come together had them all sprinkled with the infusion. His own people stood unharmed, but the Coranieid fell dead, every one of them, and his own people rejoiced.

May Eve was near, and Lludd had the island measured, and in the centre, where is now Oxford, he had a pit dug; he ordered a tub to be filled with the strongest mead that could be brewed, had the tub lowered into the pit, and the place covered with a silken sheet. Then he, and he alone kept watch.

Darkness came but he could see two dragons on the ground. They fought, and presently rose high in the air on the great wings and fought more fiercely than ever. A frightful scream made the king shudder, but he stayed firm; and after the scream the two dragons came hurtling down; they fell on the sheet, dragged it down with them into the tub; and there began drinking. They drank the tub dry, and fell into a sleep so profound that even magic would hardly be likely to waken them.

At once the king climbed down and wrapped the sheet tightly about them. He had them hauled up and taken to the strong place, where a stone coffin was ready for them. Here they were buried deep beneath earth and rocks, and until this day no more has been heard of them.

The joy over all the land was great, and Lludd was honoured; but he gave credit to his brother for the wise good counsel.

And now he, and he alone, must deal with the third problem. First he had a great feast prepared, and set out food and wine in abundance, rich and rare; but no guests were invited to eat it. Lludd waited alone, cloaked and armed, in the dark. Close beside him stood a tub filled with ice-cold water.

Out of the shadowy silence came the sound of sweet music, lulling him, almost compelling him to sleep; but he plunged quickly into the cold water. He did this more than once, whenever the faintest drowsiness came over him; then out of the shadows came a creature carrying an immense hamper which he filled with the food and drink that were set out. The hamper was so heavy it was a wonder he could lift it, much less carry it away; but he did — until Lludd ran after him shouting:

"Stop thief! Who are you who steal my provender? This is the last time you will attack my house, unless you can overthrow me in combat."

The huge man was so startled that he dropped the hamper. Lludd ran at him with his sword and the creature defended himself with great vigour. They fought fiercely, for they were well-matched. For a time Lludd seemed to be hard-pressed, but at last he delivered a skilful stroke, and had his opponent lying on the ground.

"Mercy. Spare me!" he cried. "You have overcome me and I yield."

"Why should I spare you?" demanded Lludd, his sword still drawn.

"Because I shall restore all that I have taken from you; I shall swear allegiance to you and be your liege man."

Lludd listened, and sheathed his sword, accepting the thief as his new liege man. And in him he found a valiant champion. So ended the three plagues of Britain, and Lludd ruled the land in peace.

Powel and Rhiannon

Powel Prince of Dyfed was one of the great lords of Wales. He ruled over wide lands and used to go from one to another, from one palace to another. His favourite was Arberth, and it was there that he met with a great adventure and found his true love. There had been a day of hunting, the prince and his company had dined, it was a pleasant hour of freshness and they went out from the palace to a green mound a little beyond it, and stood looking around.

"Do you know the spell laid upon this mound?" one of the older men asked Powel. "It is said that whoever sits here will either come into some hurt and danger, or else see a great wonder."

"As for hurt and danger", Powel replied, "I have faced them often, I can face them still. But I would gladly see a wonder."

He sat down, and his comrades with him. And there he saw riding along the highway towards them a most beautiful lady in a golden gown, mounted on a milk-white horse.

"Who is that lady? Does anyone know?". But none had seen her before.

"In courtesy let one of you go to meet her" — he looked at one of his men, who rose and walked quickly down to the road and towards the lady. But she was now riding away, and although she rode slowly and he walked fast, even running, he could not come up with her.

He went back to the prince, who bade him go to the stable and saddle a horse and ride to meet the lady. The man obeyed without delay, and off he rode swiftly — but still he could not catch up with the lady.

"Well, let us go home", said Powel, and they went back to the palace for the night, and spent the next day there. On the second day the prince ordered a swift horse to be brought, they all climbed the mound again, and Powel bade one of his men ride down to meet the lady, who was again approaching them on her white horse. Again the man rode very swiftly, still the lady seemed to be riding slowly, but he could not come up with her.

Again they went home, and the next day the prince said: "I shall ride myself to meet the lady if she appears; so bring me the swiftest horse in the stable".

From the top of the mound they saw the lady coming towards them. Powel mounted his horse and rode down, more swiftly even than in the hunt; but she was riding away from him and he could not catch up with her.

At last he called out at the top of his voice:—

"Lady, I implore you, stop and speak to me."

And she stopped as soon as he uttered those words.

"I am glad to stop and speak to you, Prince Powel. But why did you not come yourself to meet me the first time? Better for your tired horses if you had!" She was smiling as she reproached him, and he thought that lovely as she had appeared when he first saw her, she was even lovelier now.

"Lady, what is your name, and where do you ride?"

My name is Rhiannon, daughter of Hevyth Hen, and I ride on my own affairs."

"Will you not tell me where you are going?" begged Powel.

"I am riding away from my father. He would have me marry a man whom I detest; but no other whom he thinks worthy has asked for my hand. Now, there is one man only whom I would gladly wed, and that is yourself."

"And that is the greatest and best news I have heard", declared Powel happily. "For I have given you my whole heart."

Rhiannon smiled again very sweetly.

"Then listen, and follow my counsel. I shall ride home now and tell my father, and persuade him to change his mind. That will not be hard, for he knows you and holds you in high esteem. Wait for a year then ride to his castle. The wedding feast will be ready. Will you keep faith with me?"

"Indeed I shall, with my whole heart."

They parted then, and Powel went back to his own palace. His companions were eager to know who the lady was and what she had said, but he avoided all their questions. A year passed quickly, though not so quickly as he would have liked, and then he gathered his comrades and attendants together and told them the whole story. He knew the lands of Hevyth, although he had never gone there; and now he ordered preparations to be made for the journey, gifts for Rhiannon and her father, all manner of things. They set off cheerfully and came to Hevyth's palace, where they found a good welcome. The wedding feast was ready and they sat down together, Powel with Rhiannon, and Hevyth at the head of the table. There was plenty of conversation, there was music played by a skilled harper, and everyone was in the best of spirits. At the end of the feast a handsome man came into the hall and approached the high table.

Powel, who did not know him, greeted him courteously: "Will you not sit down with us?"

"Thank you, my lord, but no; I come only to beg a boon of you."

"Ask, and I shall grant it", Powel promised.

Rhiannon was looking at him with reproach.

"That is a rash and foolish promise you have made, my lord."

The suppliant laughed mockingly.

"But it is a promise, and it must be kept. This is the boon I ask, Prince Powel. The lady whom I love, alone of ladies, is sitting by you. I ask that I may have her for my own tonight".

Powel sat as if frozen.

"Who is this man?" he asked Rhiannon frantically. "I do not know him."

"He is Gwawl, to whom my father wished to marry me, from whom I was fleeing when you first met me and spoke to me."

Powel was silent, filled with shame at his own folly.

"Small use is it to be silent now", Rhiannon told him. "But small use also to reproach you. Come apart and listen to my counsel."

They withdrew beyond earshot of Gwawl and the others, and Rhiannon whispered:

"Bid him depart now but return in a year's time. Then the wedding feast will be prepared again, and I shall be awaiting him. But he must depart now, and so must you. When you go I shall give you a bag; keep it carefully, and in a year's time return carrying it, and bring all your company. Do not bring them to the hall, but leave them waiting in the orchard yonder. And you yourself must come to the hall on foot, wearing old and shabby clothes, like a poor beggar. Gwawl will be seated in the place of honour, and you must beg him for food to fill your bag, for you are starving.

"He will order food to be brought, in quantities, more than enough to fill the bag, but however much is put into it — the bag will not be filled. Gwawl will marvel at this, and you must tell him that there is a spell upon it; tell him that the bag will only fill up if a great lord, the owner of a great deal of land, should jump into it and tread the food down. Gwawl will take up the challenge, and will jump in and sink down; then you must draw the neck of the bag up above his head, and tie it firmly. Then blow your horn to call your men in from the orchard. Will you do that?"

"My lady and my love", Powel answered humbly, "I will do all you bid me."

So he turned to Gwawl.

"I promised you a boon and I must keep my promise. But will you go hence for a year, that there may be time to prepare another feast? My lady bids you return then."

Hevyth gave this proposal his support. Gwawl accepted and departed. Powel returned to his own land and waited patiently for a year. Then he called his comrades and attendants together and they rode away. Powel carried the bag, and he went dressed in poor and shabby clothes. When they came near Hevyth's palace he bade his men wait in the orchard until they heard him blow his horn; then he went on foot, like a beggar, came into the great hall where now Gwawl sat at the high table, as he had sat a year before, with Hevyth and Rhiannon.

Powel spoke very humbly.

"My lord Gwawl I beg alms. I am poor and I am starving. Will you not give me food to fill my bag?"

"That I will", said Gwawl heartily enough, for he was well pleased with himself, and he ordered the servants to bring meat and bread in large quantities. They stuffed it all into the bag which the beggar held open; but it would not fill.

"Will it never be full?" asked Gwawl.

"Not until a great lord, owning much land, jumps into it and presses the food down with his feet", the beggar told him.

Rhiannon looked at Gwawl.

"I will do that", he said, and jumped into the bag, pressing down the food. Powel drew the bag up above his head, tied it firmly, and blew his horn. His men heard and came down from the orchard, and into the hall. Powel threw off his disguise and stood in his princely dress.

"What will you have us do?" asked his men.

"What you will. You may beat the bag and what is in it with your swords".

This they did with much laughter. "There is a badger in the bag", they told each other; and this is how the game arose which is known as Badger in the Bag.

Gwawl called out piteously:

"Let me out, I am being beaten to death".

He appealed to Hevyth:

"I do not deserve such punishment".

"Truly you have had enough", Hevyth answered. "Will you not let him out?" he asked Powel.

"I will, if Rhiannon bid me."

"Let him out", said Rhiannon. "But make him first promise to go away and never come back, never to seek revenge, and to give up all thought of me."

"Will you promise these things?", Powel demanded, and

feebly Gwawl replied: "I shall; only let me out."

Powel untied the bag and Gwawl crawled out, very bruised and sore, begging for ointment to heal his bruises. He was anointed and given food and drink, and he made a solemn promise to depart and never return, to give up all thought of Rhiannon and all idea of revenge. So he departed and no more was heard of him.

The feast was a great success, with a great deal of joy and laughter, and when it came to an end Powel and Rhiannon went to their own room.

"Will you stay a while?" asked Hevyth next morning. "Or will you go now? Will you take Rhiannon with you or will you send for her? It shall be as you choose."

"I choose to go now and to take my bride with me", Powel told him. They parted in great goodwill and courtesy, and Powel brought Rhiannon his bride to his palace of Arberth. There was great rejoicing there, and the joy did not end with the wedding feast. There was music on the harp, there were gifts from Rhiannon and Powel to the musicians, and to all the guests. Never had so lovely and so kind a lady been seen, and Rhiannon was dearly loved by the people.

For a year, for two years, for three years she and Powel lived happily together. Then there were mutters and murmurs of discontent among the counsellors and great men, for Rhiannon had no children, there was no heir to succeed Powel. These counsellors came to him and begged him to take another wife. "My lord, you must have a son to follow you."

"Wait but another year", Powel told them. And before that year was out Rhiannon bore a son, as fine and handsome a child as ever was seen.

The night after his birth she lay with him in her arms, watched by her women. She was very weary, and she slept. The women watched for a time, then they too went to sleep. That was not good. Nor was it good when they awoke to find the baby gone. They had heard nothing, seen nothing. Rhiannon still slept, exhausted by her child-bearing. The women searched that room and all the rooms near; but there was no trace of the child. They were in great fear, and one of them said:

"I have a plan that will save us. There is a hound outside

that has just whelped. Let us take and kill some of her puppies and smear the blood over Rhiannon's breast and arms. Then we shall declare that she killed her son in a fit of frenzy and put him away, we cannot tell where, for she terrified us by her madness."

The other women agreed to this vile plot, and began wailing and weeping. This awoke Rhiannon, who at once looked around for her baby.

"Where is he? Let me have him".

"Alas, lady, he is gone, and it was you yourself who slew him. You awoke in a frenzy and killed him — see the blood on your arms and breast! You took him away, we were unable to follow you, for you put the fear of death into us."

"In God's name that is not true. If he is dead, it is you who slew him; if he is hidden away, then it must be you who took him, and you must know where he is. Tell me he is alive! Tell where he is and bring him to me, and I promise no harm will come to you."

She wept and pleaded with them, but they would not listen; they declared solemnly that she had killed and hidden her own baby son. Powel came in then to see his wife and his son, and stood amazed at what he saw and heard. The women showed him the blood on Rhiannon's breast and arms, they told him their foul lies. Some of the noblemen and counsellors who had followed him to see the baby boy heard the sad tale too. Rhiannon declared her innocence. Powel nearly believed her, he longed to believe her, but he had to listen to his counsellors, and they believed the women. Some of them would have had the poor lady banished or imprisoned, but Powel would not permit that.

Sadly and meekly Rhiannon asked that a certain wise old man be brought to her, for she was willing to accept whatever punishment he might decree, and she would accept sentence, and do penance for a sin she knew she had not committed.

The wise man came, he listened, and gave judgement. Rhiannon must not be banished or imprisoned, she must stay with her husband. But every day, for seven years to come, she must spend three hours in the courtyard, sitting by the mounting-block at the gate. To all who came she must recite the charge made against her, and must offer to carry them on her back into the hall.

Humbly Rhiannon accepted that sentence. There were few in the land who believed the charge, few of those who came would let her carry them, for she was still loved by the people. The sad story spread beyond the Prince's land.

Now in one of the lands bordering those of Prince Powel there lived a good man Teyrnon, and his wife. He was not wealthy, but he had a good stable of fine horses. He and his wife lived very happily, with only one grief — that they had no children. There was another thing too that plagued them. The finest mare in all the stables had ill luck with her foals. Every year she foaled, but every year the new-born was taken away, by whom none could tell. This happened always on May Eve.

"It is happening too often; we must not let it happen again", said Teyrnon's wife.

"Indeed we must stop it" he agreed. "But how? The grooms vow that they keep watch — but they can give no account of what happens."

"Then you must go yourself; tomorrow is May Eve. You must stay hidden, armed and ready, and watch."

So next evening Teyrnon went to the stable alone, cloaked and armed. He stood there watching, listening. Some time later the mare dropped her foal, and at the same time the window above her stall opened and a great hand and arm appeared, seized the new born creature and would have carried it off, but Teyrnon drew his sword and slashed off the hand and arm. The foal was dropped, there was a frightful scream and the thud of rushing feet. Teyrnon ran out to follow and capture the monster, whoever it was; then he remembered he had left the stable door open. He returned, and on the threshold he found a tiny baby boy, wrapped in golden silk. Very gently Teyrnon took him in his arms; the mare was licking her foal, a fine little creature; all was well. Teyrnon carried the baby into the house, to his wife's room.

"Are you asleep?"

"I was for a little, but I am awake now. Have things gone well?"

"Indeed they have". He told her how he had put the monster to flight and saved the foal.

"And just look what treasure I have found!" He held out the baby and she took him, cradling him in her arms and fondling him, looking down at him with joy and tenderness.

"Listen, dear husband, I have a plan. I am known to be in bed, I have not been well these last few days", which was true, although her illness was not grave. "Call my women, show them the baby, and tell them I have suddenly been brought to bed. They will believe it, and will be glad."

"That is a good plan", agreed Teyrnon, "and now at long last we shall have a son."

He called the women, who came running and who exclaimed with joy at the birth of a son.

"He must be baptised", Teyrnon said after a few days. "What shall we call him?"

"Call him Goldenhair", said his wife. "Look, his hair is already growing, thick and rich and as golden as the silk that wrapped him."

So the baby was christened and was called Goldenhair. He grew rapidly in body and in mind; tall, strong, and quick beyond his years. It was a time of great happiness for his foster-parents, and no child was ever more loved and cherished. When he was only four years old he was like a boy of seven. He loved horses and spent much of his time in the stables.

"He must learn to ride", said his foster-father.

"Indeed yes; and what better horse could he have than the foal born on the night when you found him?", said his foster-mother.

"That is a good idea. It is a fine horse now, but not too large. I will have it trained and made ready".

Teyrnon spoke to his head groom and the young horse was trained, though not much training was needed, for it was a gentle creature though swift and strong, and Goldenhair sat easily and fearlessly in the saddle.

As he grew from babyhood into boyhood his foster-father often looked at him.

"Is there not a look in him of Prince Powel?" he asked his wife. They had both seen the prince in his youth.

"I have often thought so. And I have thought much of the poor Lady Rhiannon. Never have I believed, never *can* I believe she was guilty of killing her child. I am sure now that he was stolen by that monster who tried to steal the new foal, and whose arm you cut off — never was a sword-stroke better given. Now I beg you, dear husband, to take our dear Goldenhair to his father's court. The Lady Rhiannon has suffered long enough."

"As soon as he can ride so far, I will take him", promised Teyrnon.

And so it came about. It was not long before Goldenhair could ride well enough to go with Teyrnon and two other companions to the palace at Arbeth. There at the gate by the mounting-block sat Rhiannon. She told her sad tale and offered to carry them, but Teyrnon said: "I shall walk there, and so will my companions."

Young Goldenhair leaped down from his horse, standing tall and strong before his true mother, who looked at him with a slightly puzzled expression.

"Come with us, lady, I beg you; I have something to say to Prince Powel that concerns you closely."

Rhiannon followed them into the hall. Powel was there with his chief counsellor and kinsman, Pendaran. Powel greeted Teyrnon courteously; he looked closely and long at Goldenhair.

"Who is this?"

"He is your own son, my lord, and the son of the Lady Rhiannon. He was stolen from her in childbed by a monster."

Then Teyrnon told the whole story. Rhiannon listened, nearly weeping for joy.

"Now is the end of all my care and sadness", she told Teyrnon. She took her young son in her arms, and he came to her gladly, and to his father. Never was there greater joy.

There was a great feast, where Teyrnon sat with Powel and Rhiannon, with Goldenhair and his two comrades, and with Pendaran.

"What is his name?" the latter asked.

"My wife, his foster-mother, named him Goldenhair."

"And now his own mother has named him Pryderi — the end of care."

That was agreed, and henceforth the goldenhaired boy was known as Pryderi, son of Powel.

"Let me have him now, for training in all he must learn and know", Pendaran begged Powel.

"But what of Teyrnon, his foster-father?" said Rhiannon.

"He must remain foster-father, and you with him", Powel told Pendaran. "You must be comrades from now; Pryderi will go from time to time to stay with you, most noble Teyrnon, and with your lady wife."

"That indeed would have been my prayer to you", answered Teyrnon.

Powel would have given him gold and jewels and much treasure, but good Teyrnon would take nothing at all.

"I am well content to leave our foster-son with his true parents. My wife will rejoice. She will rejoice, too, at your promise to send him to us from time to time."

There would be sadness, too, in his wife's gentle heart at losing the child whom she had so dearly cherished. But she would rejoice in the knowledge that young Pryderi was at last with his mother and father, and that Rhiannon was filled with great joy.

The Dream of Macsen

Macsen, Emperor of Rome, slept deeply, and as he slept he dreamed. This was his dream.

He was travelling through a river valley, always climbing, until he came to a mountain; and from the mountain top he could see more beautiful lands than any others he had ever seen. Rivers flowed towards the sea; at the mouth of the widest river he saw a city with a castle and many towers. Beyond the mouth of the river a fleet of ships lay at anchor, one of which had planks of silver and gold. An ivory bridge led to this ship. It seemed to Macsen that he walked across the bridge, sailed in the ship and came to an island. There he came to a castle where the gate and door both stood open; so he walked into a splendid hall, with a golden roof and golden doors. Two youths were sitting at a table playing a game like chess on a silver chequerboard; but it had only one king, and the game was to help him to escape from a party of pursuers. The men were all of gold, the two players were dressed in rich brocaded silk, each with a circlet of gold on his head. Near them in a tall ivory chair sat a dignified old man, who was also wearing a circlet of gold on his head. He held a golden rod in his hand, and a fine tool with which he was cutting pieces for the game. Beside him, on a golden chair, sat a most beautiful lady. She wore a golden gown with pearls and other jewels about her neck, and a circlet of gold and gems on her head. Such beauty Macsen had never seen, and to his delight the lady rose to greet him, and they sat down together in the golden chair. And then Macsen awoke from his dream.

He awoke with one thought in his mind. That lovely lady had taken his whole heart. There could be no other in all the world whom he would make his bride and his empress. His heart was filled with sadness and longing. He went through his days like a man in a dream. He would not ride with his men, he would not go among the people, or attend feasts or any gathering. Much of the time he slept, or half-slept, hoping always to dream that dream again.

At last his chamberlain and chief counsellor came to him with a grave warning. The people were complaining about him; that they never saw him, that he did not appear anywhere. Macsen listened, and said:

"Summon a council of the wisest men in Rome, and I shall tell you all why I am so sad and withdrawn."

The wise men came and heard his dream, and then they advised him to think hard and recall as well as he could where his dream journey had begun, then send messengers out to discover the way. This counsel Macsen followed, so messengers were sent forth, in every direction, but within a year they all returned, looking glum. Nowhere had they seen anywhere even remotely resembling the place which the emperor had recalled, and had tried to describe to them.

"Better now that you go yourself", one wise man told Macsen. "The way may become clear to you as you go." Macsen obeyed; memory guided him as it could not guide others, and he came to the place where his dream journey had begun. Thence he could direct messengers, giving them a clear description of the way; the valley and the mountain, the rivers, the ships and the castle.

This time they came to their journey's end, and in due time brought Macsen the tidings he desired. They had seen the island, they had sailed across and come to the open gate of the castle, into the splendid hall which was exactly as the emperor had seen it. The young men played their game, the old man cut new golden pieces, the most lovely lady in her golden gown sat in her golden chair as if it were a throne.

They had fallen on their knees before her.

"Hail, Empress of Rome."

"Why do you mock me?" she had said.

"We do not mock you, lady. We come from Macsen the Emperor. He has seen you in a dream, and he will have no other lady to be his empress. He will never be happy until he takes you as his bride."

"I think you speak the truth, yet I find it hard to believe what you say."

"We do indeed speak truth. Will you come with us, lady, or do you bid the emperor come to you?"

"Better that he come to me."

The messengers returned with speed to the emperor and told him the news he most longed to hear. At once he set out, following the way he knew, and so he came to the land which was Britain; to the ships and the castle with the open gate and open door.

It was all just as he had seen it in his dream, as his messengers had found it: the young men at their game, the old man at his craft, the lady in her golden chair. As in his dream, she rose to welcome him; they embraced, and that night he slept with her.

In the morning she asked for the fee of her lost maidenhood.

"Ask what you will", Macsen told her. She asked that she might have this island of Britain and all the islands that lay beside it, to the west, to have and to hold as her own. This the emperor most gladly granted her. Then she summoned hosts of men, not for warfare but for the building of roads across the island, from north to south, from east to west, from one great castle to another. The emperor had earth brought from Rome to mix with the earth of Britain in the grounds of the castles, and one of these was Caer Llion.

The lady's name was Helen, and she was known as Helen of the Hosts because she could summon hosts of men who obeyed her as they would have obeyed no one else.

They did not return to Rome, the emperor and his empress. For seven years they stayed happily in Britain. But in

Rome the people were far from happy, and there was much discontent. There was a custom that if the emperor were absent from Rome, in some other part of his empire, for seven years, he would not be welcome to return, but would have to remain in exile while a new emperor was elected. This was done, and Macsen's successor sent him a strange letter:

"If you come, and if ever you come to Rome . . ." — no more than that. Macsen replied:

"And if I go to Rome, and if I go."

He did go, and he laid siege to the city, but on the way he conquered France and Burgundy.

There was no easy victory for him in the siege, nor was there victory for his rival. But then came help from Britain. The brothers of Helen, Cynan and Gadeon, those young men who had sat playing at the chequer board, came to his help. They watched the attack, the plan of besiegers and besieged. Then Cynan said to Gadeon:

"I have a better plan. Let us wait until noon, when both sides stop fighting and withdraw to dinner. Then the defence will be weak."

"That is indeed a good plan", his brother agreed. At noon next day they climbed the wall, on tall ladders, followed by a great company, and took the city by surprise. It was not long before the usurping emperor sued for peace, and the siege was at an end.

Then Macsen said to Cynan and Gadeon:

"You have saved my city and empire, and now I make you captains of a great host, so that you may go where you will and take over any part of my dominion you choose."

The brothers thanked him and their sister the empress, and they parted in great amity and mutual gratitude. After a progress of subduing and taking possession of distant parts of the empire, Cynan asked Gadeon:

"Will you stay here or will you return to Britain?"

"I would choose to return to Britain", Gadeon answered.

"And I", said Cynan, "would gladly stay here."

So they parted in affection and goodwill, and Gadeon came again to his own country of Britain.

And so ends the dream of Macsen and what came after it.

BRITTANY

The clutching hand appears here too, but this time the owner is followed by the valiant prince — and so the beginning of a happy ending. Giants appear too, as in Scotland; evil powers are known to exist, but generally they remain in the background.

The differences between the four countries are subtle; the affinities are strong and clear.

The Golden Pears

There was a king once in Brittany, not king of that whole land, but of a small kingdom. He was happy enough, but he would have been happier if he had been wealthier. He had six daughters all in need of a dowry, and two sons, Yann and Claudik.

One of his greatest treasures was a pear tree, which every year bore three large silver pears. If he had plucked these, they would have made at least part of a dowry for his daughters. But every year, on a certain autumn night, the silver pears turned to gold, and the king, driven by greed, always waited for that; but never did he pluck the golden pears, because every year they were stolen during the night by an unknown thief.

His son Yann had a great liking for gold and for worldly possessions, and next year he offered to keep watch for three nights, to guard the pears and, he hoped, to catch the thief. As darkness fell, he came to the orchard, with his pipe and a bottle of cider, and sat down by the tree. He had a smoke and a drink, the night was warm, and he fell asleep; during the night he awoke to find one of the pears gone. Now Yann had made a bargain that one of the golden pears would be his, the one on the north of the tree, which was the largest. To his relief this was still there; it was the pear in the centre that had been stolen. This one had been intended for his six sisters. "Too bad"; said Yann to himself. "But it could have been worse. It might have been mine that was stolen."

Next night he managed to keep awake, and nothing happened. On the third night he again drank rather too much cider, and again he fell asleep; when the awoke, the pear on the north side was gone: his pear. He made a great fuss about that, and he had little sympathy from his sisters.

His brother Claudik was kind. "I'll keep watch tonight", he offered. "And if my pear isn't stolen you may have half of it."

Claudik took no cider with him; he did not smoke, but he did take a sharp sword, and his flute on which he played very well. He walked up and down and round the tree, playing a cheerful tune to keep himself awake; and nothing happened. Nor did anything happen on the second night; but on the third

113

it suddenly grew very dark. An owl screeched and flew up out of the tree and away. Then a huge hand and arm appeared; the hand seized the last pear, and was carrying it away when Claudik drew his sword and slashed off the hand. It fell to the ground, the pear clutched in its fingers. There was a wild yell of pain, and a great gust of wind blew through the orchard.

Claudik took the pear from the clutching fingers and put it into his wallet. He was about to throw away the hand when he had an idea. It was dripping blood, the wounded arm must also be dripping blood, and he might well be able to follow the trail. So, stuffing the hand as well as he could into his wallet, he began to run, following the trail of blood drops out of the orchard. The darkness had lifted, the moon was shining, and he could see quite clearly. The trail led to the edge of the forest of Kranon, and there it stopped.

"So that's where he went, whoever he is. He must be a huge giant, judging from his hand", thought Claudik. "And I expect he'd be glad to have his hand back. I must think about this."

He turned and went home to the palace, hid the severed hand, and next morning presented the golden pear to his father, who was greatly pleased.

"Better give my half to my sisters", said Claudik kindly.

He remembered a wise man he knew, a good physician who lived in the town, and went to him to ask for some lessons in healing. These he quickly learned; he thanked the good man, paid him well, and bought a box of an ointment which would heal any wound.

The next day he went to the market square, where everyone came and where all sorts of news and gossip were to be heard. Just as he arrived a herald was reading a proclamation. The giant-king of the Forest of Kranon would give the hand of his daughter, the lovely Flower of Kranon, to the man who could heal him of a grievous wound received in battle.

"In battle?", said Claudik to himself, with a smile. "In fruit-stealing."

He went home, packed the hand into a knapsack and put the ointment in his pocket, took his flute and a stick, and walked off to the edge of the forest. This time he went further, a long way in among the dark trees, until he reached a high wall and a barred gate. Beside the gate stood a hut, and at the door of the hut sat a little old woman.

"Dear lady of the gateway", said Claudik, taking off his cap and bowing politely, "will you be very kind and open the gate for me?"

The old woman smiled, very pleased by his good manners.

"If you wish I can let you through, but I warn you against it. Many a good man has entered the forest and gone up to the castle, but none has ever returned. Some have tried to heal the giant-king's hand, and have failed; some he would not even allow to try."

"I would like to try all the same", he said. "I have something the king may be glad to have restored to him."

"Well, God go with you and bring you safely back. Now, when you have gone a little way you will see a narrow track leading to the left off the main path. Turn off there and follow it. It will lead you to the back door of the castle. There you must take your flute and play. Do you know the dance-tune Gabadao?"

"I do; I have often played it."

"That is good", said the portress, "for it is the princess's favourite tune. She loves music greatly, and hears little of it. Life here is little better than imprisonment for her. When she hears you play that tune, she will come out and dance to it."

"And on my way back I shall play it again for you, kind lady."

The old woman smiled and sighed, and opened the gate. Claudik walked through, and along the broad path. Soon he came to the narrow track of which the kind old woman had told him, and turned to follow that. The trees grew thick and dark, and from some hung a fearful burden: human corpses. Here were his predecessors in this adventure. Claudik sighed, and went on. The great, grim castle came in sight; he walked to the back door and began to play the dancing tune on his flute — such a merry tune as can rarely if ever have been heard there.

The door opened, and out came a girl who was indeed well-named Fleur, or the Flower of Kranon. She was lovely and graceful in her movements, but wore a desperately sad expression. Then she began dancing to Claudik's playing, and as she danced a smile came to her face; she looked happy, and lovelier than ever. Claudik danced too, opposite her, while he played. At last he stopped, breathless.

"And now, dear Princess, will you lead me to your father?"

"May we not finish our dance first? When you have met my father there will be little chance of another one."

"We'll see about that. Maybe what I have brought him will please him."

"Then take off your shoes and follow me on tiptoe." — Very quietly Claudik obeyed. The princess led him through a hall, up a wide staircase, splendidly lit; the walls were hung with tapestries, and also with golden pears.

"My father's", Claudik remarked cheerfully.

They went into a large room, richly furnished, with an immense bed in one corner. On the bed lay the giant, groaning frightfully. He was guarded by two dragons, who advanced on Claudik as soon as they set eyes on him. Their eyes were indeed as red as flames or as rubies, their golden scales flashing and glinting. Claudik took his knapsack containing the hand, and waved it at them. They were at once subdued. They sank back, and even began to wag their tails like good dogs.

Claudik walked forward to the bed.

"Who are you?" roared the giant, staring at him. "But it doesn't matter. Whoever you are, I'm having you roasted for my lunch. I'm hungry. Hi there, you two!"

The two were cooks, big fellows who came forward to seize Claudik. There was a fire on the hearth and a spit in front of it. Claudik waved the knapsack with the hand first at one, then at the other, and they fell back meekly.

Then Claudik took his flute and began playing that merry dance tune. The princess, who had been watching in terror, smiled and began dancing again. The two cooks danced, heavily but happily. The dragons danced, sliding along the floor, curling and uncurling their tails, rising up, falling again, very effectively and gracefully, their ruby-red eyes and their golden scales flashing and gleaming.

Finally the giant threw off his coverings, scrambled out of bed and began dancing too, in his own awkward, lumbering way; but he was enjoying it, he was roaring not with rage or pain, but with laughter.

Claudik himself danced, but as he still carried the heavy knapsack, he was the first to stop and sink breathless on the floor.

The cooks stopped too, and collapsed on the floor, panting. The dragons slid over to the hearth, coiled themselves up neatly and went to sleep. The princess stood watching. The giant hobbled back to his bed and lay gasping and panting.

Claudik, holding the knapsack carefully, went and knelt by the bed. The giant put out his hand to seize him; but a touch of the severed hand hidden in the knapsack immobilized him. "What have you there?" he growled.

"Something of yours which you will be glad to have back."

Claudik drew out the hand, and took the box of ointment from his pocket.

"If I restore and heal your hand, will you keep your promise and give me the princess in marriage?"

"I shall", said the giant in a new and feeble voice.

He held out his wounded arm. Very gently and deftly Claudik rubbed the stump with the ointment, rubbed the hand, put it in place on the arm, and anointed the join.

The giant rose. He felt no pain, the hand was perfectly joined, as flexible as ever. He did not try to seize Claudik. Instead he walked over to his daughter, took her by the hand and gave that hand to Claudik, mumbling something that may have been a blessing; at any rate it was not a curse.

The cooks rose and set about preparing dinner. There was plenty of food in the larder: meat and game, fruit and vegetables, with plenty of excellent wine. The dragons awoke and began sliding across the floor, frolicking and playing with each other; the cooks had to step carefully over them but there was no accident, and there was plenty of food for the dragons too.

The giant had completely changed. He was amiable, rather dull, rather a bore, and every now and then he would just drop off to sleep. After a few days, Claudik and the princess left the castle, and walked along the narrow track,

along the broad path to the gate where the kind old woman
welcomed them, almost speechless with joy and wonder.

Claudik did not forget his promise. He took out his flute
and played the dancing tune, and both she and the princess
danced happily together. Claudik invited her to come with
them to his father's palace, and this invitation she most happily
accepted.

There was a great store of treasure of all sorts in the giant's
castle, which he had said was to be the princess's dowry. (It is
impossible to describe the change that had come over him).
Claudik had thanked him, and said that all he wanted was the
collection of golden pears. These he and the princess were
carrying between them.

They walked on, back through the forest, to the king's
palace where Claudik was welcomed by his mother and father
and sisters with floods of joyful tears. Yann kept calm but
seemed pleased enough, especially when he was given a

golden pear. Each of the princesses was given one, and the rest Claudik gave to his father.

Claudik and his bride stayed for a time — a time of feasting and dancing and rejoicing — and then returned to the castle in the forest. The old woman returned with them, as housekeeper. The cooks stayed on, and so did the dragons (now grown harmless and amiable). Before long, the giant-king died. Claudik and Fleur settled down there together, and in due course brought up a family in the castle, where they all lived in great happiness. They cleared away many of the dark trees. When Claudik's father died, he left him the wonderful pear tree, and they had this transplanted to grow by the castle. Every year it bore silver pears which turned to gold. The prince and princess used to gather two, but always left one to glow with its lovely light in the dark nights.

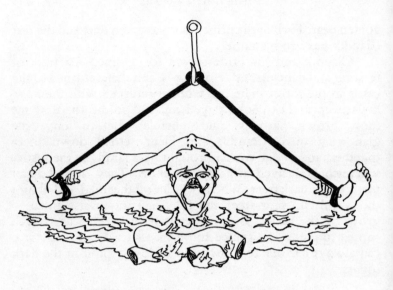

The Sun Princess

In the village of Keranborn in Brittany there lived a young miller, Ewen Kerepol. He was unmarried and lived by himself. One morning when he went to open the flood-gate and let in the water to turn his mill-wheel, something unexpected and unwanted came in with the stream — a large eel. It lay there without moving, and Ewen lifted the lever he held in his hand to kill it.

"Do not strike me, do not hurt me, Ewen", the eel begged. "I am not what I seem; I am not an eel but a princess under a spell. And you, if you will, can set me free."

Ewen was astonished but not incredulous. Strange things did happen, he had heard about spells and enchantments, so he replied courteously:

"How can I set you free? Tell me, and I shall try." Ewen was both brave and kind, and although (or perhaps because) his life so far had been quiet and uneventful he was quite prepared for an adventure.

"If you go tonight to the ruined castle up there at the top of the hill", the eel told him, "and stay until morning, you will begin the breaking of the spell; if you go again tomorrow and the next night, then you will have broken it completely and I shall be free. Only I warn you, it will mean danger for you."

"I'll do it", said Ewen. "I have no one depending on me. A man must take a bit of a risk from time to time, and I'm tired of doing the same thing every day."

The eel swam away, Ewen went to the mill, met his servant Gabic, and began the day's work. That night he went up to the castle, a grim ruined place, entered the kitchen and sat down by the hearth. He had brought his pipe and a bottle of cider. Drinking the cider made him feel drowsy, so he looked round and saw a bed in the corner; he lay down, drawing a cover over himself. He soon fell asleep, though not for long, for he was wakened by a great noise of stamping and roaring. By the dim light he saw three giants storm in. They sat down at the table and began to play cards, quarrelling and swearing all the time.

After a while they paused.

"There's a queer smell here", growled one.

"It's the smell of a Christian", said the second.

"Let's find him", said the third.

And this they did, almost at once.

"He's a spy and a thief", said the first.

"Come to discover and steal our gold", said the second.

"Let's put an end to him", suggested the third.

They threw Ewen on to the floor, put the mattress on top of him, and began jumping on him.

"He won't be able to look for gold now", they said at last, with evil laughter, and off they stormed and stamped, out of the castle and away.

Dawn came, and with it the princess, freed for a little from her enchanted form. She pulled away the mattress, knelt down by Ewen, and looked at him with infinite pity in her eyes. He was breathing faintly, and she poured into his mouth some drops of an elixir of life from a small bottle. He stirred a little. Then she rubbed a healing salve into his wounds and bruises. Presently he sat up, and smiled at her.

"My brave Ewen. You have begun my release from enchantment. Can you rise? Can you walk?"

"I can indeed; I'm feeling fine", Ewen assured her as he stood up.

"And can you bear to face a second ordeal? It may be even worse than this?"

"I can, and I will."

The princess left him then, and Ewen went slowly back to his mill. It was still early and he had a bit of sleep before Gabic came. He said nothing about his experience, and the two men worked together as usual. When darkness fell Ewen went back to the castle.

He lay down on the bed and waited, taking care this time to stay wide awake. Soon there was a fearful din of roaring and stamping, and the three giants came in. Again they sat down to play cards, again they quarrelled and swore at each other, until there was a noise in the chimney, and down popped an evil-looking goblin.

"You're enjoying your game, are you", he said mockingly, "and never thinking of the spy that's here. Can't you smell him?"

"Faith and I can, now you mention it", said one giant.

"He's there, on the bed", the goblin told them, and went back up the chimney.

"I see him", growled the second giant.

"And he isn't there now", said the third, with a wicked laugh, as he picked Ewen up and threw him on the floor. "Let's play football with him", he suggested. This amused the others, and they began kicking poor Ewen about, picking him up, and hurling him back on to the floor.

"And that'll be the end of him", one of them decided; the others agreed, and off they went laughing and roaring.

Ewen lay very still. Dawn came, and again the princess came quietly in. She knelt down by Ewen, looking at him with infinite compassion; she felt his heart, and listened for his faint breath. Again she poured some drops of the elixir into his mouth, again she rubbed his poor battered body with the magic salve. He stirred a little, opened his eyes, looked up and smiled at the princess, who helped him to his feet.

"Ewen, my hero; you are the bravest man I know. Now I am two parts free. But you have suffered dreadfully. Can you bear a third ordeal? It may be even worse than this!"

"I'm not giving up now", Ewen told her. "I'll get the

better of these giants. And tomorrow you will be altogether free and yourself again, princess."

Her face was full of gratitude and admiration. Away she went, and Ewen returned to the mill.

The day passed quietly in work with Gabic, and at nightfall he went up to the castle again.

He had not been there long before the three giants strode in, and this time they saw him at once.

"Still alive, are you", roared one. "But you won't be for long. There'll be no recovery for you this time!"

They kindled a fire on the hearth, and when it was blazing, one of them picked up Ewen and fastened him on the spit that stood on the hearth.

"That will settle you, my fine fellow. You'll sizzle and roast very well."

This was agony beyond even the suffering of the other two nights. Ewen fainted with the dreadful pain, and when the giants felt convinced that he was truly dead, they went out roaring with laughter.

In less than a minute the princess came running in, her face streaming with tears. She gently lifted Ewen off the spit, poured a few drops of the elixir into his mouth, and softly but firmly anointed all the burns on his poor face and limbs and body. It was a long time before he came back; she felt his heart and pulse again and again, and used up every drop of the elixir, and the very last rub of the magic salve. At last she felt life creep back into him, and his eyes flickered open to find himself lying in her arms. Passionately she kissed him, and you may be sure that this was more effective in bringing him back to life than either the elixir or the magic salve.

Very feebly he rose to his feet.

"It is beyond telling, what you have done, Ewen", she said. "Now I am entirely free; and now you shall have your reward. Can you walk with me, down to the cellar?"

He could, though only painfully and with a limp. In the cellar were two enormous barrels.

"This one is full of silver, and that one is full of gold", the princess told him. "Take as much as you can carry and come back for more. It is all yours, if you want it."

Ewen looked at her sadly.

"Is it not enough? Would you like some jewels too?"

"I do not want either silver or gold or jewels", he told her. "I want one thing only, and that is your hand in marriage, for I love you dearly."

The princess smiled, and a joyful radiance spread over her beautiful features.

"You shall have it, for I love you too, my dear Ewen. Now listen until I tell you what we must do. I am the Sun Princess, and my father and mother are King and Queen of Gascony. I must go to them now and tell them you have set me free. But in ten days from now I shall come to Brittany again, to the town of Plouaret which is not far from here. There you must meet me and we shall be married.

Meanwhile, tell no one about it, except your good servant Gabic. He is trustworthy. Bring him with you as groomsman and witness, but speak to no one on the way."

Ewen joyfully promised to do all she bade him. They parted lovingly, and the princess went away so swiftly that Ewen could not follow her. Home he went to the mill; Gabic arrived for the day's work, and Ewen told him the whole story. Gabic said little, but he looked pleased.

On the ninth day, Ewen gave him a good new suit of clothes, and next morning they both dressed carefully in their best, and rode off each on his horse. Gabic had spent the night at the mill, and they left very early, before anyone in the village was up, so that no one saw them go.

But as they rode out of the village they passed the cottage of an old and wicked witch. Her daughter, who was beautiful but also a witch, nearly as wicked as her mother, had tried to marry Ewen, but he would not have her.

"Good day to you, Ewen, and where are you off to so early, and you so finely dressed?" asked the witch, coming down to the gate and out on to the road.

Ewen did not answer.

"Maybe it is to your wedding you are riding?"

"It is", said Ewen, shortly.

"Then you must come in and drink to your bride." But Ewen shook his head and rode on.

The witch came hobbling after him.

"Then take this apple I have just plucked from my

orchard. It is the finest I have ever seen. You may be glad of it when you are thirsty."

She slipped it into his pocket and hobbled back to her cottage looking very pleased with herself, and very malicious.

They rode on, Ewen and Gabic. The sun came up, and Ewen felt thirsty. He found the apple in his pocket, forgot or did not realise who had put it there, and ate it. At once he collapsed over his horse's back, into a profound slumber.

Gabic jumped off his own horse, stopped Ewen's horse, half lifted and half dragged Ewen to the ground, laid him on the grass by the side of the road, and tried to waken him. But he lay as if drugged or spellbound.

Gabic left him lying in the grass, tethered his horse beside him, and rode on to Plouaret. There he had not long to wait before a fine carriage drawn by four dromedaries came along, in which sat the princess looking very beautiful. The coachman stopped, the princess looked out:

"Where is he? Where is Ewen? What has happened?" Gabic told her, and she looked overwhelmed with grief.

"Go back to him; when he awakes, give him this handkerchief, which is the colour of the stars. And bring him here tomorrow."

Gabic obeyed. When he came back to his master, Ewen was beginning slowly to awake. Gabic gave him the handkerchief, and the princess's message. Ewen was deeply distressed and ashamed. He had failed his bride. There was nothing to do now but to return home. As they passed the witch's garden she and her daughter saw them and laughed maliciously.

Very early next morning Ewen and Gabic rode out again. When they came to the witch's house, there she was waiting for them, at the garden gate.

"And where are you off to, so early, and both of you dressed so fine?"

"Mind your own business", Ewen growled.

"Now don't be angry with a poor old woman who wishes you well. Wait — I have something to tell you."

Ewen did not stop, but the witch ran after him and slipped an apple into his pocket, then went back to her cottage, laughing an evil laugh.

Ewen hardly noticed her. He rode on, the sun came up, he felt thirsty. Without thinking he found the apple in his pocket, and ate it. Again he fell asleep, again Gabic had to take him off his horse and leave him lying in the grass, the horse tethered beside him.

Again poor Gabic rode on to Plouaret. The fine carriage came along, the coachmen stopped, the princess looked out anxiously.

Gabic told her sadly that it had happened again. She sighed deeply. "Go back to him, and when he wakens give him this handkerchief, the colour of the moon. Bid him come tomorrow, and there will be no reproach."

Good, faithful Gabic rode back to the place where he had left his master sleeping. Ewen slowly awoke, Gabic gave him the handkerchief and the message. Ewen wept bitterly in shame. But there was nothing to do but ride back to the mill. They did not see the witch, but she was there all the same, hiding behind her wall with her daughter, laughing with malicious glee.

On the third morning they set out very early, riding swiftly. As they passed the witch's cottage she called to them, but neither answered. Again she ran after them, and without speaking again, slipped an apple into Ewen's pocket. He should have remembered; but perhaps she had muttered a spell which dulled his memory. Anyhow, as they rode and the day grew hot, he felt the apple in his pocket, ate it, and for the third time fell asleep. For the third time poor Gabic had to ride on alone to Plouaret and tell the princess.

She looked worn out with grief, and tears stood in her eyes. "I cannot come again", she told Gabic. "He will have to come and find me. But give him as token this handkerchief, the colour of the sun. If ever he comes to my palace and finds me, let him show me these three tokens. And now farewell, good Gabic."

Off she drove, looking very sad, and very grim.

At his third awakening Ewen was broken-hearted. They rode home to the mill, and next morning Ewen said:

"I must ride off and find the princess. However long and hard the way to her palace, I must find it. But you must stay here and look after the mill, my good Gabic; if I do not return, the mill is to be yours."

Before leaving, he rode up to the castle, which was no longer haunted by the giants. He took a good supply of gold and silver for his journey, and gave some to Gabic, then very early in the morning he rode off.

He rode far and wide, everywhere asking where the palace of the Sun Princess might be. No one could tell him, but everyone was kind and hospitable to him, for he was so gentle in manner and so sad. He had good lodgings every night, and food enough for his journey; and at last he came to the edge of a forest. A hut stood there, and outside the hut was an old man. A green path led into the forest.

"Where does this lead beyond the forest?" Ewen asked the old man.

"I do not know. I have never gone further. But I had a brother who once went deep into the forest. For all I know he may be living there now."

Ewen thanked him and said, "I shall ride on and perhaps I shall find him, and give him your greetings."

"Go then, and God be with you", said the old man kindly. Ewen rode on till he came to a clearing deep in the forest, and there stood a cottage. By the door stood an old man who greeted him kindly, and to whom Ewen spoke respectfully. He gave him his brother's greetings, and asked whether he knew where the palace of the Sun Princess was, whether it was in or near this forest.

"That I cannot tell you, for I have not moved from this place", said the old man. "But it may be that I can help you. I am master of all the beasts of the forest. The wolves come to my call. They roam far afield, and it may well be they have seen this palace."

He climbed onto a high rock and blew a horn which he carried. There was a sudden rush of paws, and many hundreds of wolves came running. They did not look at Ewen, but only at their master, who spoke to them in a strange tongue. Then he said sadly to Ewen:

"They do not know; they have never seen a palace. But do not lose hope. Ride on a day's journey into the forest, and you will find my other brother. He may well be able to help you."

He bade Ewen spend the night with him, which he

thankfully did, and next morning he rode on. At nightfall he came to a cottage where another old man welcomed him. Ewen gave him greetings from his brother and asked whether he knew of the palace of the Sun Princess.

"Alas, I do not myself know; but do not be sad. I am master of all the birds of the air. Rest here tonight, and in the morning I will call them and it may well be that one of them will know."

So Ewen spent that night with his kind host. Early next day the old man mounted a rock, took up his horn and blew a summons. From every quarter flew vast flocks of birds great and small. Their master spoke to them, and they replied.

"They do not know", he told Ewen. "But the eagle has yet to come. He flies so far, he is always late. Ah, here he comes" — and a great eagle flew overhead, swooped down, and listened to his master. He replied in their own language, and the old man turned to Ewen.

"He knows where it is. He will take you there. Only we must find food for him; he asks for twelve sheep to be killed and prepared." "Can these be found?" asked Ewen. "Indeed I think so. There is a man not far from here who has a great flock. Have you money to pay him?"

"I have indeed", said Ewen. So it was all arranged. Twelve sheep were bought and killed. Their bodies were loaded on to the eagle's back. Ewen sat there too, and the combined weight was so great that the eagle could hardly rise from the ground. But he did at last, and flew off on powerful wings. Ewen fed him from time to time with great gobbets of meat.

At last the eagle began to swoop down. His load was lighter now. He had brought Ewen to the gates of a city.

"You can see the palace there, not far off", he told Ewen, who by this time had managed to pick up a smattering of eagle language.

"You have been a good friend to me", said Ewen gratefully.

"It has been a pleasure to serve you", the eagle assured him. "Do not hesitate to call me if you need me again. For the meantime, however, farewell."

He flew off and Ewen walked into the city, to an inn

where he took a room, announcing himself as a merchant with some rare goods. The city was gay with flags and hangings, and the most beautiful flowers. The innkeeer told Ewen that the Princess of the Sun, whose great palace was to be seen from every part of the city, was to be married that day in the cathedral, to the son of the King of Portugal.

"The Prince and his parents are at the palace. After the wedding there will be feasting and dancing. Oh, it is a great time for us all."

"That I can well believe", said Ewen. "Well, now I must go up to the cathedral square."

Washed and refreshed he walked up to the square, and stood near the cathedral. A procession came along, at the end of which rode the Sun Princess, in her carriage, a lady-in-waiting beside her. Ewen stood in full view, holding out the handkerchief, the colour of the stars. The Princess saw it, and memories flooded into her mind and heart. She called to the coachmen to stop the carriage.

"Go to that merchant", she bade her lady, "and ask him the price of that handkerchief which he is holding.

The lady obeyed.

"The only price I ask is the privilege of kissing the princess's left foot."

"That is ridiculous", said the lady-in-waiting. "The princess will pay you with gold."

"I do not want gold; I will take no other price."

The lady went to the princess.

"He shall have the price he asks", said the Princess. "Now, bid the coachman drive me back to the palace, for I shall not be married today. And have the merchant brought to me at the palace."

The coachman turned coach and horses, and drove back. Ewen was summoned, and followed a messenger up to the palace, into the room where the princess sat. He went forward, knelt before her, kissed her left foot, and withdrew.

He spent the night at the inn, and next morning came again to stand outside the cathedral, holding out the handkerchief coloured like the moon, with lovely silvery radiance.

Again the princess had the carriage stopped, again she

sent her lady-in-waiting to ask the price of the handkerchief:
"I ask nothing but the privilege of kissing the princess's
right foot", Ewen told her.

"He shall have what he asks", said the princess, and bade
the coachman drive back to the palace, saying: "I shall not be
married today."

Again Ewen was taken to the palace, into the hall, up to
the princess. He knelt and kissed her right foot, and withdrew.

On the third morning he took the handkerchief coloured
like the sun, golden and brilliant so that it dazzled the eyes. He
stood in his usual place, the procession came along, the
princess stopped her carriage and sent her lady-in-waiting to
ask the price of that most lovely handkerchief.

"I ask the privilege of kissing the princess's hand", said
Ewen.

"He shall have what he asks", said the princess, and again
bade the coachman drive back to the palace, saying: "I shall not
be married today."

Ewen was brought into the hall where she sat. He knelt
and kissed the hand of the princess. She smiled at him, and
bade him stay to dinner. He was given a place of honour near
the princess.

At the end of dinner she said to the King of Portugal, who
sat beside her: "Sir, I have a story to tell you and a question to
ask. A princess was held under a cruel enchantment until a
brave man, at great danger to himself, and after much
suffering, set her free. If that princess were your daughter,
what reward would you give her rescuer?"

"I would give him my daughter's hand in marriage", said
the king.

"I am that princess, and there is my rescuer", she told
him.

The king was dismayed; but he was a man of honour and
would not go back on his word.

"We had better go home tomorrow", he said quietly to
his queen and their son. The queen agreed; she may have
murmured to the prince that there were other princesses in the
world, and most of them had never been held under an
enchantment. They took a courteous leave, and for the fourth
time the wedding procession moved towards the cathedral.

This time the princess did not bid her coachman drive back to the palace; not, at any rate, until she had gone into the cathedral, met Ewen waiting for her at the altar, and been married to him. Then indeed they drove back in great gladness. There was a fine wedding feast, followed by days of rejoicing. The Princess and Prince Ewen — as he now was — were tremendously happy. He told her of all his wanderings and adventures.

After a few days they returned to Brittany, to Keranborn, to visit Gabic. Their journey was much easier and much swifter than Ewen's had been alone.

Gabic was hard at work in the mill when they arrived, but he dropped everything at once to give them a great welcome. He sat them down to a meal of bread and cheese and cider, which they enjoyed as much as the finest feast. They told him all that had happened, and asked how he fared. He was busy and happy, and he was about to be married to a girl in the village whom Ewen knew to be both good and pretty.

"The mill is yours for life, Gabic, and will be for your heirs", Ewen told him. "And here is money to furnish the cottage as you and your bride desire, and to keep you secure."

"And here is a dowry for your bride", added the princess very kindly, giving him another bag of gold. "And a gold brooch and necklace and earrings to wear on her wedding day. And God give you joy."

They stayed for the wedding, which was very soon, and then departed, returning to the princess's country. And no one could possibly tell which was the happier couple — the prince and princess in their palace, or Gabic and his wife at the mill. All that need be said is that they were all blissfully happy until the end of their long lives.

Yvon and Finette

Once upon a time there lived in Brittany a nobleman called the Baron de Clairvaux. His wife and he had six sons and six daughters. The castle, where they lived happily together, was large and stately; on the first floor were twelve tall windows, six of which opened on to a balcony facing east, six on to one facing west. Every morning when the Baron rode off to visit his great estate his six daughters would stand, one in each of the east windows, to bid him good day. They were so lovely and gentle, they looked like figures of Our Lady in a stained glass window. When he returned in the evening, there stood his six tall sons, one in each of the west windows, to welcome him home. They were like sculptured knights. The baron and baroness were very proud of their family, who gave them great joy.

Dearly as they loved them all, they had one favourite son — the youngest, Yvon — who was only sixteen, and yet already known for his valour, so that men called him Yvon the Fearless. His father's love was selfless, for when Yvon came to him, begging permission to go out into the world and seek his fortune, the baron let him go with his blessing.

So Yvon rode gaily off, and for three years travelled widely and had many wonderful adventures. At the end of that time he was asked to lead an expedition against the Norsemen; he set sail gladly, with a band of knights, at first on a calm sea with a following wind. Presently, however, the sky darkened, the sea grew rough, and a great storm arose. The waves dashed over the ship, breaking the mast and sweeping the little band of voyagers into the sea. Yvon surfaced, and as the moon rose he could see land. The tale tells no more of his comrades, but Yvon swam towards the shore, landed exhausted and fell asleep. When he awoke at daylight he saw far off a tall building, and began to walk towards it. As he came near he could see how large and grim it was; his father's castle would have fitted into one corner. Undaunted, Yvon marched up to the door. The knocker was far above his height, but he seized a stone and thumped with it on the door.

"Come in", roared a voice, almost loud enough to have shattered any ordinary castle; the door was opened and Yvon entered, to be confronted by a giant forty feet high. If Yvon and his brothers had stood, all six of them one on another's heads, they would have come up to the giant's chin perhaps, but no more.

"And who are you?" roared the giant, holding Yvon up to his face to see him properly.

"I am Yvon the Fearless."

"Oh, welcome young Fearless. You are in luck, I happen to need a servant so you may have the job, with board and lodging provided." At this point the giant gave rather a coarse guffaw. "You can begin at once. I'm taking my flocks and herds to pasture, and you can clean out the stable. That's all for today. You'll find that I am not a hard master. But one thing I forbid you: on no account may you enter the castle." And here again he gave that nasty laugh.

When the giant had gone, followed by his flocks and herds, Yvon said to himself. "Cleaning the stable won't take long, but why may I not enter the castle? That is exactly what I mean to do. There must be something worth seeing." The great door was not locked, so he walked in. The first room had a fireplace but no fire, and a great cauldron hung there. "I wonder what is in that?" said Yvon to himself. He cut a lock of his hair, and dipped it into the cauldron, then drew it out covered with copper.

"A new kind of soup", he thought, and went into the next room. Here too a cauldron hung over the hearth, and into this he dipped another lock of his hair. He drew it out covered with silver. "This is fine", he thought, and went into a third room, also with a cauldron above the hearth; and when he dipped another lock of hair into it, the covering was of gold. "What next?" he wondered. "Jewels, perhaps?" But in the next room he found something more precious than any jewels: a lovely girl, so fair and gentle that he fell on his knees before her. She looked at him with kindness, and yet with an expression of great compassion.

"How did you come here, my poor boy?" she asked. "Do you not know the danger you are in?"

"I have just come, and the giant has taken me as his servant. I have to clean out the stable, but that won't be difficult", said Yvon boldly.

"How little you know", the girl told him with compassion. "You will find that as soon as you sweep out a pile of dirt, ten times as much will drift in at the window. Others have tried — and suffered. But I shall tell you what to do. You must hold the pitchfork by the fork and sweep with the handle, and the work will be quickly done."

"I shall remember that", Yvon promised. "And now let us talk about ourselves. Let me tell you how beautiful you are! What is your name please? I am Yvon."

"And I am Finette", said the girl. "I am a fairy's child. The giant our enemy stole me when I was very young, and holds me captive here."

There was much to talk about, especially as they discovered almost at once that they had fallen in love with each other. Time passed much too rapidly, and Finette had to urge Yvon to leave.

"You must go at once and clean the stable."

In his happiness Yvon almost forgot her bidding about the pitchfork, and began heaving the muck out, only to find ten times as much come in by the windows. Then he took the fork by the prongs and attacked the muck with the handle, which cleaned everything out in a few minutes. Yvon then went to sit by the castle door, very much at ease, singing an old Breton song. The giant came thundering back with his flocks and herds.

"Have you cleaned the stable?"

"Indeed I have. Will you please inspect it?"

The giant, much to his surprise and dismay, could see no dirt at all in the stable.

"You have had help with this", he roared. "You must have spoken to my Finette."

"Your finette?" asked Yvon in all innocence. "What in the world is that? Is it a pet animal of yours?"

"You'll soon see!" growled the giant.

Next day he told Yvon:

"Now that you've cleaned the stable, you must bring home the horse from the mountain. That is all you have to do today. I am not a hard master."

As soon as he had gone, Yvon went into the castle to talk to Finette.

"I have only to catch and bring home the horse", he told her. "That will be easy. I am good with horses."

"But you do not know this horse", Finette warned him. "He will breathe smoke and fire upon you and destroy you. But if you take the bit that hangs behind the stable door and throw it into his mouth, he will immediately become gentle and docile."

"I shall remember and obey", promised Yvon. "And now, to talk of ourselves!" Once again they spent the day happily talking about themselves and their future. Yvon asked Finette to come with him as his bride to his father's castle. In such talk they almost forgot the time, but Finette remembered, and sent Yvon off to take the bit from the stable and to go to the mountain for the horse. There he saw a great proud steed that came galloping towards him breathing smoke and fire. Yvon threw the bit into his mouth, and the horse came gently towards him, allowed him to mount, and bore him back to the stable. Then Yvon went to sit by the door and sing another Breton song, until the giant came thundering along with his flocks and herds, roaring:

"Have you brought my horse down from the mountain?"

"Certainly I have. He is here in the stable. What a noble horse he is, and how gentle and docile! Will you go and look at him?"

"You have had help", roared the giant when he came back from the stable. "You have seen my Finette."

"You keep talking about that finette creature, what is it?"

"You'll soon find out."

Next morning the giant told Yvon:

"Today you will go down to Hades to collect the rent due to me. After that, the day is your own to spend as you please. You cannot call me a hard master", and again he laughed his horrible laugh. Yvon went straight to Finette, as soon as the giant was out of sight.

He had thought it would be easy to clean the stable and catch the horse, but he had not the faintest idea how he could even discover Hades, let alone collect the rent due to the giant. Again Finette told him the way.

"Do you see that great rock? That is one of the entrances. Knock three times with this stick. A devil will open the door and ask what you want, and then how much. Answer him: "Only as much as I can carry away."

"I shall do as you bid me", promised Yvon. Then he sat down beside her, and began to talk of their marriage, the return to his father's castle, and their life together. At last Finette had to urge him to go. He went to the rock, struck it three times with his stick, and a demon appeared, asking:

"What do you want?" — "The rent you owe the giant." — "How much?" — "Only as much as I can carry." — "It is as well you said that. There, take what you want."

The ground inside the cave was covered with gold and jewels, as if with sand and pebbles. Yvon filled a sack he had brought with him, but did not fill it too full. He could carry it without too much effort, and he took it back to the castle, where he sat down outside the door singing a Breton song, until the giant came stamping back.

"Well, have you been to Hades and have you brought me the rent that is my due?"

"I have; here it is in this sack. Please examine it."

The giant opened the sack and poured out the gold and gems.

"You have seen my Finette. She must have helped you."

"Please tell me what this finette creature is. Can I see it?"

"You will; tomorrow."

Next day the giant gave Yvon no task at all. He himself went off without his flocks and herds, and came home about noon, complaining of a headache caused by the heat of the day.

"I shall sleep", he told Finette. "Meanwhile, go to the door where you will find my servant. Cut off his head and put it into a pot on the fire. Boil it, and when the broth is ready, waken me."

When the giant's snores began to rumble like thunder, Finette brought Yvon into the castle, into the kitchen, where she cut his finger slightly over a chopping block. Three drops of blood fell on to the block.

"Now help me to fill the broth pot, with anything and everything."

Together they collected piles of stuff: rags and bones, boots, an old rug, and stuffed them into the pot.

"Come quickly", said Finette, leading Yvon into the

room where the cauldron of gold hung above the hearth.
Dipping into this, she made three golden balls which she put
into the bag at her girdle. In the next room she made two balls
of silver, and in the third, one ball of copper. Then they fled
swiftly from the castle.

Presently the giant awoke and called: "Is the broth
ready?" One of the three drops of blood replied: "No, not
yet." So he went to sleep again, awakening before long, to
demand: "Isn't the broth ready yet?" — "It will be ready
soon", answered the second drop of blood from the block. "It
is simmering." Again the giant fell asleep, and again he awoke:
"Surely the broth is ready now?" "It is ready", replied the third
drop of blood, and the giant rose and barged into the kitchen.
The broth-pot was bubbling and steaming, but the smell from
it was not very appetising. Yet the giant was hungry, so he
ladled out a bowlful of a very peculiar mixture. The taste was
worse than the smell; the giant picked out an old boot, then a
piece of sacking, and realised that he had been tricked. Roaring
and dancing with rage, he rushed out of the castle, looked all
around, and saw in the distance the escaping lovers. His
immense strides brought him near them in a very short time.
Finette looked back in terror:

"I have a spell; but if it fails we are lost."

She threw the copper ball towards the giant, saying:

"Copper ball, copper ball,
   Save us from the giant's thrall."

It might not be great poetry, but as a spell it worked. A
deep gulf opened in the ground between fugitives and pursuer.
Yvon laughed, and mocked the giant, but Finette urged speed.
They fled on, while the giant danced in fury. Then he had an
idea; he tore a tree up by the roots, flung it across the chasm
and began to wriggle across it on his belly. By this time
Yvon and Finette had reached the sea-shore, but no ship was in
sight. Finette threw one of the silver balls, calling:

"Silver ball, silver ball,
   Let no danger us befall" — and immediately a beautiful
vessel came sailing towards them, with all sails unfurled. They
ran into the sea, swam to the ship, a rope was let down and
they climbed aboard. The ship sailed off, but by this time the
giant had come to the edge of the sea. Giants like witches dread

water, but his fury was greater than his fear and he strode into the waves, throwing huge rocks at the ship, without however doing any great damage. Finette threw the second silver ball, crying:

"Silver ball, silver ball,
   Help us, lest in death we fall."

A bright silver sword rose from the depth, no hand holding it, but it swung and lunged at the giant, cutting and piercing him until he gave up, and splashed back to the shore and collapsed.

"Darling, clever Finette", cried Yvon. "We are safe. That is the end of him." — "The end of him, perhaps, but not of our peril. He has a witch-godmother, very powerful in magic, and I fear her pursuit and her vengeance. Promise me, dear Yvon, not to leave me until we have reached your father's castle, and are married there."

"My foolish love. What can harm us now? Indeed I would not leave you for a moment."

Their voyage was swift and delightful with a calm sea and following wind, and soon they reached the coast of Brittany, a part which Yvon had known since early childhood, only half an hour's walk from his father's castle. They were set ashore, and the ship vanished without trace.

Standing there, so very near home, Yvon for the first time looked at Finette critically. She was indeed lovely, and he knew her to be loving and gentle and valiant, but her dress was very odd, not at all what would be expected of his bride, not at all suitable for her first appearance before his parents and sisters. He imagined his parents and sisters finding fault with his Finette (though indeed the faults were all in his imagination) and said:

"Dearest, let me go on alone to the castle and bring you a fine robe and cloak, and a horse for you to ride with me to be welcomed by my parents."

"Oh please do not leave me! There is danger still. I am afraid!"

"Don't be silly! I shall be gone only an hour or less, for I shall ride back on a swift horse."

"You will forget me as soon as you enter the castle."

"How could I forget you anywhere?"

"Promise me not to linger, not to eat or drink anything, and to speak to no one but your father, and to him only briefly?"

Yvon promised gaily and went off, head held high in triumph at his return; he sang as he walked, and when he came to the town round the castle he heard other people singing, found everyone gay, the houses decorated. He was recognised and joyfully welcomed, and told that one of his sisters had just been married to her chosen bridegroom, a noble youth, and that this was a day of rejoicing. Yvon walked quickly up to the castle, through the courtyard and into the great hall, welcomed on every side, most of all by his father to whom, remembering his promise, he spoke briefly, telling him that he had brought home a fair bride. Then he ran upstairs to his sisters' rooms, chose a fine dress and cloak, then down and out to the stables to mount a swift horse. As he rode towards the gate, leading a palfrey for Finette, he met a most beautiful lady, who held an apple:

"Noble youth", she said in a seductive voice with a tantalising smile, "I know you must not linger, but I beg you in courtesy to me to taste this apple."

Yvon accepted the apple, bit into it, and looked around in sudden bewilderment, as if newly roused from sleep.

"What am I doing here, riding away? I ought to be in the castle with my father, helping to receive our guests." He leaped down, gave horse and palfrey to a groom to lead back to the stable, and offered his hand to the lady whose beauty was not gentle and gracious like that of Finette, but had something strange, almost terrible about it. She had bewitched him, and before they entered the castle he had asked her to marry him and she had accepted. Finette was entirely forgotton. He presented the lady to his mother and father as his bride, and the wedding was arranged.

As for poor Finette, she waited an hour, two hours and more, sick at heart, knowing what had happened. Darkness was falling and it was cold. She set out to walk to the town, but stopped when she came to a small cottage, hardly more than a hut, with a cowshed next to it: a poor place, but it had four walls and a roof which would shelter her for the night. An old woman was sitting at the door of the shed, about to milk her cow. She looked at Finette and scowled:

"Be off with you; I want none of your sort hanging about." She saw nothing of Finette's beauty, only her rather odd and shabby dress. "Please, of your kindness, will you give me shelter for the night, even to sleep here in the cowshed?"

"Oh, very well; but you must pay for your lodgings."

"That indeed I shall", said Finette. She took one of the golden balls from the bag at her girdle, and threw it into the milk pail, saying:

"Golden ball, golden ball,
 Help me when to you I call."

The pail was filled with gold coins, the old woman clutched it with a screech of delight, and curtseyed mockingly:

"All that I have is yours my dear", she cackled, and ran off into the town. "Now I shall live in luxury."

Finette entered the cottage, which was merely a hovel.

"Golden ball, golden ball,
 Help me when to you I call" — she spoke the words again, tossing the second ball ahead of her. The whole place glowed with gold; floor, walls, and roof, the bits of furniture all shone like the sun. Finette roused the dim embers on the hearth to a blaze, went out and milked the cow, heated some milk for supper and went to bed, so tired that in spite of her unhappiness she fell asleep at once.

Meantime the old woman had made very good speed into town, and went straight to the castle where she told the steward about this miraculous gold. He tested the coins, assured her that they were sound, good money, managed to abstract some for himself, and warned her not to tell anyone about it. She meant to keep the secret, but could not resist telling the friend with whom she spent the night, and that friend told one or two others, all of course in strict confidence. The story was soon common gossip, and the old woman found herself followed by children calling her a witch.

As for the steward, he could not put that lovely glittering gold out of his mind, nor the story of how it was made. He was a bachelor and thought himself extremely eligible. A wife with that gift would be worth having, and surely he could persuade the girl to marry him? He was after all a good-looking fellow, with a good position at court. So next morning at daybreak he went off to the old woman's cottage. It was easily found, for the golden glow could be seen through the trees which surrounded it. Finette sat by the window, lovely to look at though less lovely in the steward's eyes than the gold surrounding her.

The steward went boldly in, announced his name, and asked her to marry him. More amused than angered, Finette just laughed at him.

"Beware how you mock me. I am a man of influence. I could have you arrested and punished as a witch."

"You are a persuasive wooer", Finette answered lightly. "Surely no woman could possibly resist you."

"That is our way in Brittany. Now choose: marriage or imprisonment, possibly even worse."

"I must think for a moment. Oh, look. A cinder has fallen from the fire. Please will you take the tongs and put it back into the fire?"

"Certainly, my dear", said the steward, very amiable now that he thought he had won her. He took the tongs.

Finette uttered a spell: "Abracadabra! May the tongs stick to your fingers and your fingers to the tongs until sunset." And they did. All day long the steward's fingers stuck to the tongs, which he had to keep using, for bits of cinders kept falling out on the hearth. Finette was not there; she had gone down to the shore to look and wait for Yvon. At sunset the tongs dropped off, the steward scuttled out of the hovel and ran home. He was much too ashamed to say anything about his experience.

Finette came sadly back, but she was not alone for long. The mayor of the town too had heard about the magic gold; he too was unmarried, he too thought that any woman would be lucky to have him as a husband, and a wife who could make gold would be worth marrying. Off he went to the golden cottage, brilliant in the woods, and made his proposal as abruptly as the steward had done, with the same tactless threat of arresting Finette as a witch if she refused.

"And I'm prepared to stay all night until you consent."

Finette pretended to consider this.

"I don't think you would make a very attentive husband. You have left the door open, and it is cold."

"Sorry, my love. I'll shut it at once."

As the mayor touched the handle, Finette spoke her spell: "Abracadabra! May you hold the door and the door hold you until dawn." And all that night the door kept shutting and opening back and forwards, dragging the fat mayor with it. He was cold, breathless, and wretched. At first light of dawn the door released him and he fled back to town, too humiliated to tell anyone about it. Finette slept all night, awoke to see the unwanted wooer depart in haste, but she was not long alone. A report of this wonderful gold had come to the castle chamberlain. He marched solemnly to the cottage, opened the door and advanced upon Finette — a tall grim figure in black, with a black velvet cap on his head and a sword by his side. Like his predecessors he was unmarried and had decided that the gold-maker would marry him.

"Do you own this cottage and its contents?" he asked sternly.

"I do, sir."

"Then I shall do you the honour of making you my wife and assuming the care of your property."

"Sir, you do me too much honour. I am unworthy of that high rank."

"Stop talking and sign this contract."

"But I cannot write."

"That does not matter. You need only mark a cross here, at the foot of the document. See, I am making the same sign, for a gentleman does not need to know how to write."

As he put the document on the table and stooped to make his mark, Finette ran out of the cottage and into the cowshed and into the cow's stall. The cow began to back out. The chamberlain came rushing in, caught the cow by the tail and dragged her out. Then Finette uttered her spell: "Abracadabra! May you hold the cow's tail and the tail hold you until you have gone round the world." And off the cow rushed at incredible speed, dragging the chamberlain after her. It sounds rough on the cow, but this was a magic journey at magic speed, and did her no harm. As for the chamberlain, he was dragged and bumped, whirled in the air, over land, over sea, and at the end of the journey came back to the town quite exhausted and battered. The cow went placidly to her stall, the

chamberlain went thankfully to bed, hoping that no
rumour of his adventure
had got about. He was not
popular, being proud and
pompous, and the towns-
people would have made
the most of any story to his
detriment.

No one at the castle had
any time to think about him
or about the mayor or the
steward. Preparations had
been made for the wedding
of Yvon to his strange,
beautiful, but somehow ter-
rifying bride, who appeared
to have bewitched him
completely. He had,
however, told the baron
that he had brought home a
bride, so he and his wife
accepted her. That morning
they set out, baron and
baroness, Yvon and the
lady, in the great coach
towards the Abbey Church
of Saint Maclou where the
wedding was due to take
place. A procession of their
household accompanied
them, headed by the cham-
berlain, including the
mayor, and, at the end, the
steward. These three
worthies were none of them
in very good shape. The
townsfolk looked on with-
out cheering or rejoicing —
a very different affair this

from the wedding of Yvon's sister, where everyone was happy. No one cared for this bride, but the people all kept their thoughts to themselves. Yvon was silent, like a man in a dream.

About a mile from the castle one of the coach wheels fell off. It was replaced, but it fell off again, and this time the axle was broken. They tried to mend it, but it would not hold. Then the steward came forward, bowing to the Baron, and said: "My lord, there is a lady in a cottage in the wood who has an excellent pair of tongs: very adhesive. Perhaps she would lend them; they would, I am sure, make a strong axle." The baron sent some men with a courteous request. Finette listened and at once agreed to lend her tongs. They proved to hold the wheel strongly, it was fixed to the coach and the coachman drove on. It had not gone far, however, before the floor fell out. The coachman drew up at once, a carpenter was summoned, the floor replaced — but it fell out again, and yet a third time. Then the mayor came forward.

"My lord, there is a lady there in the cottage in the wood, who has a fine golden door. Perhaps she would let us have it, to serve as floor for the coach." "Convey my compliments to the lady and my hope that she will be so good", said the baron. Some men ran with the message, which Finette received with charming courtesy, willingly allowing them to take the golden door. It replaced the broken floor, and again the coachman drove on. But just as they came in sight of the Abbey the horses stopped, all of them as of one accord, and would not move another step — though clearly not one of them was lame. Neither the whip nor any coaxing would make them move a hoof. Two other horses were brought, but they too refused to move. Then the chamberlain spoke.

"My lord, there is a lady in the cottage in the wood who has a remarkable cow, very strong, very swift-moving, better than six horses. Perhaps she would lend us the cow to take us to the church."

Again the baron sent a most courteous, deferential request, and again Finette agreed with equal courtesy to lend her cow. The horses were taken out of the shafts, the cow was harnessed in their place, and she did not stand still. The coach was drawn forward at top speed, passing the gates of the

Abbey, turning round and heading rapidly for home, without stopping until they all reached the castle. There the cow was released, and she ambled off, back to her shed. It was now too late to do anything about the marriage itself, and everyone was too shaken and bewildered to contemplate any further travelling. The baron and baroness decided that they would hold the banquet all the same, and this was good news for all their guests.

They were all seated in order, the baron at the head of the table with Yvon and the lady on his right, when it occurred to him that some courtesy ought to be shown the mysterious lady in the cottage in the wood, who had so kindly lent her tongs, her door, and her cow. If the last loan had not proved exactly what was desired, that was surely not the fault of the owner. So the baron decided that an invitation be sent, and a page rode off at once. He found Finette weeping. When he gave the baron's message, Finette answered proudly:

"If your master will not come to me, then I shall not go to him." On hearing that, the good baron was abashed and contrite:

"Indeed I have failed in courtesy. I shall ride myself, and beg the lady to return with me." At the cottage he greeted Finette with apologies and deference, begged her to come with him, took her up behind him on his horse, and brought her to the castle and the hall, where he led her to the seat on his left hand. The company were full of curiosity, which gave place to admiration as they looked on her gentle beauty. She must surely be a princess from some far land. The steward, the mayor, and the chamberlain were embarrassed and ashamed, fearing that she would recognise them and tell the baron of their behaviour and the insults they had laid upon her. But she gave no sign at all. Of all the company, only Yvon looked at her with indifference. He was like a man in a dream or one bewitched, with looks only for the lady by his side, who received them and his compliments with scorn. She was sitting opposite Finette, and if looks could kill, Finette would not have lasted for long!

As for Finette, she was in the depths of despair. There was only one source of help. Taking the third golden ball from the bag at her girdle, she uttered her plea:

"Golden ball, golden ball,
  Help in my greatest need of all."
The ball became a beautiful golden goblet. Softly Finette
asked the steward to fill this with mead, and offer it to Yvon.
"Ask him to drink to my health, as I shall do to his." Yvon
drank a little, without looking at Finette, set the goblet down
and turned again to the lady, who smiled maliciously. Finette
wept silently.

The baron rose: "Let us drink", he said in his warm kindly
voice, "to the lady who so graciously helped us, and now
honours us with her presence." Everyone rose to drink the
toast with great good will, and Yvon had to rise with them. He
lifted the golden goblet to the level of his eyes, and began to
tremble. In the clear gold he saw pictures of all that had
happened; his meeting with Finette, their flight and their
voyage, the scene on the shore. Memory returned, he knew
her as his true love and realised his fault. He looked at her
entreatingly, with love, humility, and contrition.

"Finette, my own love, forgive me", he cried, falling on
his knees before her. Finette forgave him lovingly. He
presented her to his parents as his true bride, and related to
them and the company all the adventures since his landing on
the giant's island. The hall was filled with rejoicing, and
Finette looked as radiant as the golden sunlight. No one gave a
thought to the malignant witch lady, but next day the servants
had a tale to tell of a hideous old hag who had flown out of the
castle and away, on a broomstick! People agreed that she must
have been the giant's witch-godmother, then dismissed all
thought of her from their minds.

Yvon and Finette were married next morning in the
Abbey Church of Saint Maclou. There was neither delay nor
accident on *that* journey. At the feast afterwards the rejoicing
was exultant. Everyone was happy. The chamberlain, the
mayor, and the steward danced wildly, for it was clear that
Finette would never show any sign of remembering them. She
had infinite tact, kindness, and a wonderful sense of humour.
In return they gave her their profound gratitude and loyalty.

No lady was ever so deeply loved as Finette, Yvon's fairy
bride. Her kindness and goodness were even greater than her
beauty. She cared for everyone. Long after she and Yvon, their

children and their grandchildren were dead, she was remembered with love and veneration. She lived as a legend, and her statue stood in the hall of the castle until the castle itself crumbled many centuries afterwards. The sculptured figure held six balls — one of copper, two of silver, and three of gold.

Sources

Six of the Scottish tales in this volume come from J.F. Campbell's *Popular Tales of the West Highlands*: 1, "The Battle of the Birds"; 3, "The Smith and the Fairies"; 4, "The White Pet"; 5, "The King of Lochlann's three Daughters"; 6, "Grania and Diarmid"; 7, "The Knight of the Riddles". "Deirdre", (2), comes from Alexander Carmichael's *Deirdire*.

Of the Irish Tales; 8, "The King of the Pipers"; 11, "Changelings"; 12, "The Sunken Palace"; 13, "The Bride from the Sea", are from Thomas Crofton Croker's *Fairy Legends and Traditions of the South of Ireland*. "The Brown Bear of Norway", (9), comes from Legendary Fictions of the Irish Celts, by Patrick Kennedy; and 10, "Guleesh" from Douglas Hyde's *Beside the Fire* and from Joseph Jacob's *Celtic Fairy Tales*.

The three Welsh legends: 14, "Lludd and Lleflyns"; 15, "Powel and Rhiannon"; 16, "The Dream of Macsen", are from the *Mabinogion* translated by Gwyn Jones and Thomas Jones.

The Breton tales: 17, "The Golden Pears", and 18, "The Sun Princess", are from the November and June 1901 numbers respectively of *The Strand Magazine*. "The Legend of Yvon and Finette", (19), is from *Fairy Tales* by Edouard Laboulaye.